Fly Like the Clouds of Time

2022 California Poets in the Schools
State Anthology

Brennan DeFrisco, Editor
Fernando Albert Salinas, Assistant Editor
Meg Hamill, Executive Director

The title of this anthology, *Fly Like the Clouds of Time*, is adapted from a poem by Patrick Robinson

Cover Art by Sole Hopkins

California Poets in the Schools
P.O. Box 1328
Santa Rosa, CA 95402
    Meg Hamill, Executive Director
    David Sibbet, President of the Board

ISBN: 978-0-939927-30-2

Poetry is the lens we use to interrogate the history we stand on and the future we stand for

Amanda Gorman

The remarkable thing about children is the blankness of their pages. Blank pages contain everything – hope, potential and beginnings. Blank pages are clear and positive, uninfluenced and untarnished, unwrinkled and completely open to interpretation and imagination. Best of all, blank pages are waiting to be filled with as much brilliance as they can contain, with all the ink from every pen.

There is magic that happens when children start to fill their own blank pages. There is a raw tenderness, an innocent bravery, that we as adults will never quite capture again. Imagine going back in time and remembering our first experiences of love and joy and reverence. Picture our first triumph over adversity, back when our parents were gods and the world was a buffet, and we believed everything could still be good. Or better, remember, if you can.

Let us never stop being the people we are as children. Let us never forget. We get older, and education, and experience, and redundancy fill our pages, and we become numb, jaded, complacent. We get so caught up in the rat race and paper chase of adulting, lost in the fine print of grown-up business, that we actually think we become completely different people once we are big, and have bills in our name, and are responsible for other human beings. But we don't. Our curious wonder and excitement about it all remain, just underneath the surface. All it ever takes is a prompt, a little courage, and inspiration.

I invite you, as you read this book, to be inspired. Realize that no matter how old you are, there is more ahead of you than behind you. So much of life is still fresh and unopened – go taste it. Let these youth take you to the place inside yourself where you believe in superheroes, and the good guy always wins. Life is a journey full of endless destinations. Embrace what is contained here, what the children have filled their blank pages with. Let yourself hope and marvel and wonder. Some more. Let the fullness of these youths' experiences help you to find and fill your own blank pages again.

Nazelah Jamison
Author of *Evolutionary Heart*

Contents

I Am A Colorful World

Paper Dreams

i am a single silver star
shining in the darkness,
a small hopeful light
drowning in black waters.

no one knows when i remember the
words that pound through my mind,
screaming like a river
under a mossy plank bridge.

i am a lonely lighthouse
overlooking the sea,
a thin sun-gold ray searching
for survivors.

for people like me.

am i the perfect porcelain doll
obedient daughter, sister, friend?
yarn head heavily bowed,
fragile body quietly still?

whatever i am,
i'll be by your side until the end.

i am a paper crane
strung in a child's bedroom,
made of love and dreams.
a wind breezes through.

my
wing
rips.

i am a wire sailboat
bobbing in a puddle.
abandoned, battered,
sinking.

but
i will float.

i am wildflowers in the sun,
laughter on the wind, because
i am alive

and i am grateful.

Vienne Voong, Grade 9
Lowell High School, San Francisco County
Allison Kent, Classroom Teacher
Susan Terrence, Poet-Teacher

Paint Me

Paint me with dark brown hair like freshly overturned soil.
Paint me with blue eyes like the ocean. Draw me jumping into the
water with a large splash to swim with the gentle giants, the whale
sharks. Picture me in Casa Roja, Costa Rica with long stretches of
white sand beaches, hordes of deadly Terciopelos and emerald
green and ebony black-green and black poison dart frogs in water
bottles. Picture me casting a fishing line far out into the distance
with a gentle splash as it hits the water to bring in a fish larger than
the human mind can process. Imagine me held by my ankles on
the side of a boat, pain wrenching at my ankles but all worth it for
the rubbery feel of a gray whale sticking its head up to be pet.
Imagine the pain of the stinger of a warrior wasp being driven into
my ear with a red-hot pain of 1000 smoldering needles piercing my
eardrum, the mark not disappearing even 6 months after. Draw
me sinking my teeth into soft mushroom wellington the flavor
nourishing my taste buds. Imagine me standing over a bucket for
babies to bathe in (that I have bathed in before) but this time it
holds the evil face of a stonefish glaring up at me with a desire in its
eyes for me to die. Imagine me standing under a curtain of leaves,
just leaving the smallest rays of sunlight to filter in.

Finn McCauley, Grade 3
Montecito Union School, Santa Barbara County
Karen Luna, Classroom Teacher
Kimbrough Ernest, Poet-Teacher

I Come From

I come from grasslands and busy streets
I come from forests and walks on the beach
I come from dry hills rolling endlessly
I come from blond first generation
I come from blue for as long as I know
I come from short fury and sad smiles
I come from gamers that recreate
I come from thinkers and helpers with PhDs
I come from builders that make where I stand
I come from changers that control what goes by
I come from people who think like me
Who say, "close the loop" and "wow" when they are proud
I come from people who believe in never giving up and
Learning how to fail

Sadiesimone Tappan, Grade 8
Salmon Creek Middle, Sonoma County
Tanya Turneaure, Classroom Teacher
Jackie Hallenberg, Poet-Teacher

Where I Am From

I am from
the stars and the ocean
I came from the horizon
where the sky meets the sea
I am from the sand
rough from the waves
always persistent
I am from the seaweed that washes up
onto the shore
My eyes are the sparkles
and the glitter
that the sun makes
on the water
My voice is a birdsong
My mind is the ocean depths
and my soul
is the night sky

Lucianna Buchheister, Grade 7
Coastal Grove Charter School, Humboldt County
Jenny Rushby, Classroom Teacher
Julie Hochfeld, Poet-Teacher

My Mind

My mind is the control panel of my body,
with so many buttons and levers,
it works day and night.
Like jeans, there are so many pockets
filled with dreams and memories.
My mind is like the bottom of a ship
where the imagination sleeps peacefully
like a tired turtle.
My eyes are back up at the top
like little lookout towers guiding me along.
My brain is like a big heap of books full of knowledge,
and like a GPS, making the turns and stops.
In a deep compartment holds all my emotions like a diary.
My mind holds many things.

Maggie Wagner, Grade 3
Vallecito School, Marin County
Dara Ferra, Classroom Teacher
Terri Glass, Poet-Teacher

My Hands Glow

My hands can grab water and rub
it all over. My hands wish to make a spiral
and make the world grow.
With these hands, I can break darkness.
If I lost my hands, the earth would be broken.
My hands remember when they felt
the shadows and the light.
My hands will keep touching items.
These hands are bright things
in this world. My hands can change
this world. With these hands
I can keep going
and going.

Aiden Nguyen, Grade 4
Loma Verde School, Marin County
Cheriann Reed, Classroom Teacher
Claire Blotter, Poet-Teacher

I Write

I write like the whispering winds
Like the path of OR-7
Like the burn of the flames
Like the leaf's trail to the ground
Like the trace of the border of hatred and hope
I write like the jagged peaks of Mt. Everest
Like the path of the howl of a gray wolf
Like a ground squirrel scribbling on the forest floor
Like an angry elk charging at its predator
Like the path of a tracking missile
I write like the mythical song of the morning birds

Nolan Ausanka-Crues, Grade 4
Montecito Union School, Santa Barbara County
Heather Bruski, Classroom Teacher
Cie Gumucio, Poet-Teacher

OR-7, also known as Journey, was a male gray wolf that was electronically tracked as he wandered more than 1,000 miles from the Wallowa Mountains in the northeastern corner of the US State of Oregon to the southern Cascade Range. OR-7 was the first confirmed wild wolf in western Oregon since 1947 and the first in California since 1924.

Pulchritudinous

I am the flash that your camera shoots
I am the white stones you find on the rocky concrete
I am the fresh pomegranate seeds your mom picks
I am the olive oil boiling on the pan at turbo boil
I am the storm you hear at 1:00 am

I am the dazzling sharp piece of glass you step on barefoot
I am the groan you make waking up to your alarm
I am the ink hitting the paper from your ball-pointed pen
I am your brain cells aching during history class
I am the sunset you watch go down at 6:30 pm

I am the voicemail you replay to hear again, again, and again
I am the broom sweeping the trash out of your room
I am the hoodie you put on when you're cold
I am the lavender waiting for a bee to collect my pollen
I am the spikes of a hedgehog that go into your skin

I am a claw clip gripping onto your hair
I am the spider in the corner of your room
that you're afraid to kill
I am the crocs you put your feet in to go help your mom
grab some stuff from the trunk of the car

I am the picture you look at over and over and over again
I am the taffy that gets stuck between your teeth
I am the ending of your amazing dream

I am Zoey Dixon's sister
I am the wind swifting through your hair
I am the warm cup of hot cocoa in your hands
I am a girl named Meeyah

Meeyah Reyna, Grade 5
Arena Elementary School, Mendocino County
Rebecca Willhoit, Classroom Teacher
Blake More, Poet-Teacher

The Unnoticed Girl

No one notices her but
She is always there
She reads a book
Called how to disappear
She is thin as string and doesn't
Eat a thing
And at the end of the day
The only one who notices her
Is me

Maple Burton, Grade 4
Coastal Grove Charter School, Humboldt County
Marjorie Bertsch, Classroom Teacher
Julie Hochfeld, Poet-Teacher

A Fifth Grade Nobody

I am the music stuck in your head
I am the cool breeze on a hot summer day
I am a book full of pages
I am your favorite smell in the kitchen
I am the wild card in Uno
I am the stars in the dark sky
I am a brain full of ideas
I am the diary that you write in
I am the last piece of your puzzle
I am a song waiting to be sung
I am the end of a road

Sophia Santana, Grade 5
Arena Elementary School, Mendocino County
Rebecca Willhoit, Classroom Teacher
Blake More, Poet-Teacher

Me and Myself

I am the blood of danger
I am a reading hazard
I am the softness of the beds
I am a feather in the night sky
I am the grass in the meadow
I am a car speeding away
I am the drums, boom boom ting boom boom ting
I am what makes the earth grow
Who am I?

Luke Rudnicki, Grade 3
Montecito Union Elementary School, Santa Barbara County
Kathy Trent, Classroom Teacher
Kimbrough Ernest, Poet-Teacher

Right In Between, It's Where I'm Caught

i am the pink in a sunset sky but also a rolling fog
a soft fresh cut bloom but an old faded pressed rose
a leaf not quite auburn, just spotted
i am an intersection on california street
always busy, but a little empty
i am an uncapitalized I in a sea of letters
almost hidden
but still distinguishable
i am a bright silver mirror smudged with fingerprints
my reflection a blurred crystal clear
i am a louis vuitton with scratched zipper teeth
and a twisted strap, raised to be flawless,
exemplary, a polished designer bag
still riddled with small mistakes,
only noticed by the ones closest to me
i am the moment of no air
just as you rise out of the pool
a moment filled with ecstasy
and a little pain
i am almost perfect
almost not
i am in between
right in between
it's where i'm caught

Madison Li, Grade 9
Lowell High School, San Francisco County
Christian Villanueva, Classroom Teacher
Susan Terence, Poet-Teacher

My Heart Is At War

My heart is at war with itself
It can't win
Its point of view is always
Changing
Moving to music
Only it can hear
It holds pain, happiness
Sadness and fun
The good and the
Bad choices
You could get
Hurt or you could find
Swing and ponder what
Might happen if
You were to get up
And play
My heart holds
Song
Happy and sad
At your best times and your
Worst
It will wait until
I am once again
Ready to move
On

Lily A. Felsenthal, Grade 6
Coastal Grove Charter School, Humboldt County
Shana Langer, Classroom Teacher
Julie Hochfeld, Poet-Teacher

School Bus

I am a school bus. Kids yelling inside me while the person that
drives me honks and says, *BE QUIET,* to the yelling kids.
I move my wheels, and travel from house to house.
I screech my wheels every time I take a big turn.
I am a school bus, but I wish I was a tree. Elegant and tall.
As it sways in the wind, people watch and stare.
But I am a school bus and I get little rest
while the kids are at school.
When they return to go home for the day,
they drop trash and drinks on my seats and my floor.
I wonder if I can be reborn as a tree.
Elegant and tall.
I wonder if I can.

Olivia Fox, Grade 4
Montecito Union School, Santa Barbara County
Heather Bruski, Classroom Teacher
Cie Gumucio, Poet-Teacher

Country Lover

I am a crazy road trip will my cousins
I am a dish rack full of clean dishes
I am a wolf howling with my friends and family
I am 11
Sometimes I am a basket of question marks
I am not good at math
I am a fluffy cuddly dog
I am a dirt road going to my gramma's house
I am a strong sunflower
I am a blue and gray mountain
I am proud and free
A country girl

Brilynn Scaramella, Grade 5
Manchester Elementary, Mendocino County
Avis Anderson, Classroom Teacher
Blake More, Poet-Teacher

Blindness

Ever since I was born, you have changed my life.
How are we connected?
Why did you take away my sight?
For many years, I struggled and fought for success in life.
There were many days when I cried because of you.
I cried because I could not do the things my peers could do.
Now, I understand that you aren't a disadvantage.
You enhanced my ability to hear and feel.
I can think differently because of you.
Without sight, everything seemed hopeless.
Years later, I realize that you are a superpower.
If someone asks if I wish to see,
I'd turn them down and say: "that's not me."
I am lucky to have you,
I wouldn't have it any other way.
I realize that you have not led me astray.

Kait Rose Guynn Grade 9
Alder Grove Charter School, Humboldt County
Julie Hochfeld, Classroom & Poet-Teacher

Ariel Ixchel Osman

My name sounds like the echoing hymn of a thousand passerines.
It sounds like the violent roar of a mighty lion declaring place in
the world.
My name rings with poetry.
My name wrings sorrow.
My name rings true.
When my name is spoken, stars chorus their bliss.
The rivers run sweet with euphoric ripples,
Crystals crack at my creativity.
At the sound of my name hearts open.
For others they may wither.
Despite all, my name is mine.
Mine to harbor,
Mine to cherish,
Mine to honor.
My name is Ariel Ixchel Osman.

Ariel Osman, Grade 7
Murphy Elementary School, Humboldt County
Crystal Fennell, Classroom Teacher
Dan Zev Levinson, Poet-Teacher

Evan

I am my ancestors who long ago walked with ceremonial choruses of bagpipes, filling the air of haggis in the land of Edinburgh. I am the boy who cherishes and enjoys the warmth of a comforting blanket in the dawn of a cold night.

I am the kid who flips pages of wonder, lost in an endless loop of pondering books like mountains that tower over fountains.
I am filled with learning lessons that are sweet but sour roses in the glazing hills. Characters swarm my consciousness, all different from the last, bringing many wills.

I am the water that runs through meadows, crystal clear, soft, traveling to hard rocky rapids. I am the air of the summer sun brightening the earth, as well as cooling the darkest caverns.
I am the fire dancing on a lit torch, exploring the unexplored with danger at the hilt of my sword. I am the strong-willed earth providing sanctuary for all, caring for and straightening those who tilt.

I am the ball bouncing across the court before it is flung into the net. The crowd screams and hollers making me feel taller, I am the determination to be better. I am the pressure of tons of thoughts in my head as the clock ticks down. I am the smile or the watery eyes, as I shake the other team's hands.

I am one with the swift pen expressing my inner thoughts and emotions. As my hand flows, the ink withers. My words wrap like a snake. Once that zone comes, time passes and my hand aches. I am the paper being crumpled and thrown away until the right draft meets my expectations.

I am the half thought and the fully developed ideas in the dawn of a cold night that are turned into a miracle, by chance.

Evan Rechner, Grade 6
Mill Valley Middle School, Marin County
Bethany Bloomston, Classroom Teacher
Michele Rivers, Poet-Teacher

A Tree, A Bird, A Rock, and A Moon

My brother is an apple tree. He stands firm in his roots
And stays stubborn to the wind. Yet he drops fruits
That can hit you in the head. Fruits that can be sweet
Or rotten.

My sister is a laughing kookaburra.
Always laughing
Always talking.
Always up in the trees.

My parents are our foundation.
They stand firm
And do it all,
Only to be unappreciated.
They still hold us up.
They make sure we never fall.

I am the Moon.
You only see me bright once.
I am half lit at all times but
you cannot see it.
I shine light reflected off of me.
I don't make my own light,
I show the light of others.

Aaron Hernandez, Grade 8
Bonita Vista Middle School, San Diego County
Katherien Kavouklis, Classroom Teacher
Johnnierenee Nia Nelson, Poet-Teacher

In The Wind

I am a grain of wheat on the
loneliest mountain
fluttering and bowing in the wind
glowing in the Sun's last golden rays
while all around me
a field does the same
I am a roll of memories in a camera
random shots, and unfinished thoughts
the starts of an undeveloped beginning
I am the words you didn't say
after turning and walking away
the happiest moments
the bitterest tears
only hours and minutes apart
I am a worn blue jacket
a starchy pair of jeans
a mop of tangled curly hair
smiling on the warm silhouetted rooftops
of the Golden City—my home

Andrei Tapus, Grade 9
Lowell High School, San Francisco County
Sam Williams, Classroom Teacher
Susan Terence, Poet-Teacher

I Feel

I feel like a beautiful creation between human and nature
I am a bird writing sound, Caw! Caw!
I am an autumn leaf rustling, patiently falling as the wind howls
I am a fiery red star twinkling in the dark sky

I feel me

I am waves crashing and sand blowing into the wind,
like souls in a river
I am a lion pounding the Earth's rock
I am the golden sun beaming the water
I am the oceans blue feeling swirling and flowing
into a sea foam green

I feel me

I am the clouds as soft as feathers and bouncy like trampolines
I am the ocean, a mirror of life showing unknown beauty
of what's deep and true
I am red, orange, yellow, green, blue, indigo, and amber coral
glowing like fireflies on the bottom of the ocean
Click! Click!
I am a whale racing towards the bright gold sun
showing my sight to the world above the water
Whoosh!

I feel me

I am a sight, show, person who is a colorful world
I am my imagination and creativity

I feel me

I am myself
I am my mind
I am my soul
I am my heart

I feel me

Skylar Ngai, Grade 6
Mountain View Elementary, Santa Barbara County
Susana Yee, Classroom Teacher
Cie Gumucio, Poet-Teacher

Walking Through A World of Language

A Distant Place

There is a place people have not found, a distant place
where the clear cool water gurgles and the white water roars
and the blue bird chirps, the hawk soars.
The fish jump strong, mountain goat sends rocks
tumbling down.
The bear and the wolves hunt, but with all this sound
it seems to be a silent place,
a calm place without voices or people playing.
What is this place? I don't know, but this is a distant place,
on a different planet maybe. This peaceful place
with the mountain watching, protecting the gurgling spring,
the bright green grass, the watchful rabbits,
the animals depend on each other in a giant link—
one of many big chains in a giant web that people disrupted
but there aren't people here
a peaceful place, an intact place, a distant place.
This place might float in the sky, covered by light clouds.
It might lie deep under the ground, maybe in space,
maybe in the dark depths of the ocean,
a bright place, a distant place.

Ramzi Bryson, Grade 5
Strawberry Point School, Marin County
Daniel Gasparini, Classroom Teacher
Terri Glass, Poet-Teacher

The Blue House

Walk across the edge of town, cross the old, abandoned bridge,
follow the path through the forest and you will find the blue house.
But beware—only those who dare to venture
shall find out.

Come at the first hour of dust, when the moon is perfectly lined
up with the sun. You will see the house fully blue.
Shining through the pane glass windows is the light
of one lonely candle.
Only one lives there,
lonely as a treasure chest.
She only comes out on the third day of June
and only walks across the path
that is paved in front of her house.
But beware—this house is the only sight of civilization
for miles on end.

No one knows what she does...
Some say she passes her time knitting,
others say they hear her sewing,
but I truly believe she is waiting,
just waiting,
for someone to show her another path
and that, my friend, just might be you.

Logan Eisenbud, Grade 5
Strawberry Point School, Marin County
Rachel Quek, Classroom Teacher
Terri Glass, Poet-Teacher

Walking In A World Of Languages

I look away when the resol blinds me
As petrichor fills my nose, I immediately feel calm
I love when the waldeinsamkeit takes over my body
But when the hiraeth comes to me, I feel downhearted
I love the vintage feel the color pardo gives me
When I feel aturdido, I know I'm in love

Lauryn Cole, Grade 8
Orleans Elementary, Humboldt County
Laura Gorman, Classroom Teacher
Dan Zev Levinson, Poet-Teacher

Resol: the reflection of sunlight off a surface
Petrichor: the smell of earth after rain
Waldeinsamkeit: a feeling of peace in the woods
Hiraeth: a homesick home that you cannot return to
Pardo: cross between grey and brown
Aturdido: to feel so overwhelmed by emotion you can't think straight

The Birth of Venus

after Sandro Botticelli

Loving too deeply
From sea foam you arose,
So effortlessly your golden locks blew
The depiction of beauty,
All eyes that lay upon you fall instantly in love
Your feet kiss the earth
Flowers bloom where you have walked
The salty sea spray blows in my eyes,
I am merely one of your many admirers
Your twinkling laugh
And your ocean blue eyes
You are no Medusa
Your gaze melts stone
The want and need to fall into the wild waves of love
Yet, eventually many drown
Your beauty harms
You bring war with love
A sweet surface with a sticky trap
Like a Venus Fly Trap,
I, too, am ensnared in your honey embrace

Sabrina Lee, Grade 9
Lowell High School, San Francisco County
Kristen Mitchell, Classroom Teacher
Susan Terence, Poet-Teacher

My Heart

My heart is filled with tunnels, twisting and turning.
As you walk through, you hear the crunch of fallen soggy leaves on
the brick floor.
By the time you make it out of that labyrinth,
you open an old hobbit door.
You grab the button-shaped doorknob and enter a fantasy land full
of wonder and beauty.
You stare at the forever sunny sky.
You walk through a field of wildflowers
until you reach a metal door
with locks encasing it.
You force the door open to find an empty room
with a single, flickering lightbulb that goes out
as you enter.
In the dim light, you see a stack of books.
You find a small cabinet in the dark, mildewy room
and pull it out to find a flashlight that brightens the whole room.
You sit there wondering why you never looked
in the place you least expect—
something so simple, but important.

Cameron Crail, Grade 5
Montecito Union School, Santa Barbara County
Marsha Brown, Classroom Teacher
Cie Gumucio, Poet-Teacher

Glass Box

Once upon a time
We lived in a glass box
And within the box
There was safety
Comfort
And ease

We could always see outside the box
But it was deemed undesirable
For we had safety
Comfort
And ease

But we grew smarter
We grew our own ideas
As the soil of our mind
Became more fertile
But we still had safety
Comfort
And ease

Yet those ideas grew and grew
And what used to be just a sprout
Was now a colossal Oak
And finally
That Oak dropped its acorns
We *were* the acorns
And we broke the glass box wide open

And stepped into the world
Where there was no safety
No comfort
And no ease
And yet
It was better

August Singer, Grade 6
Montecito Union School, Santa Barbara County
Kim Berman, Classroom Teacher
Cie Gumucio, Poet-Teacher

Impression, Sunrise

after Claude Monet

I am the sad reflections floating to hopeful land
I am the sneaky, warm ripple running across the blurry waters
I am the cold silhouettes of mystery hiding beyond the skyline
I am the hoarse breaths of optimistic passengers wishing under
    the watercolor sky
I am the loud, careful thumping of their warm hearts
I am the dark footsteps hovering the waters as silent company for
    the lonely
I am the swish of the orange in the endless sky
I am the swoosh of the waters meeting the oar in their clammy
    hands
I am the bravery of the travelers moving forward from the past
I am the eye-squinting gust of wind that rocks the boat
I am the orange ball of hope blazing a path to make way
I am the deceiving water that dried their mouths more than
    replenished
I am the temperature as cool as the waters below
I am the beginning of a new day
I am the body heat that failed to accompany through the chilling
    night
I am the swift swaying of the boat
I am the ghostly mummers of unwanted shadows
I am the figures creeping out with the horizon
I am the mystery beyond what your mere eyes can see

Hillary Situ, Grade 9
Lowell High, San Francisco County
Kristen Mitchell, Classroom Teacher
Susan Terence, Poet-Teacher

The Heart Wants to Go

The heart wants to go
to the mountains covered with snow.
It wants to run like an arctic fox in the tundra.
It wants to go to the desert where
the salt sparkles brightly in the sunlight.
It wants to go to the shiny green jungle
where the birds chirp and the sun shines
through the leaves to the ground below.

Tate Sharp-Christiansen, Grade 2
Malcolm X Elementary, Alameda County
Dr. Kathryn Mapps, Classroom Teacher
Maureen Hurley, Poet-Teacher

Sea Copses Trees

Seven waters sometimes shrouded in
Enigmatic fog
Across them: the love theme of our world

Wooden hollow ferns
Green dappled scintillate dew
Ghostly susurrations

Ten of us
Red to the humans
Electricity is uninteresting
Ever we stand the
Same as yesteryear a thousand

Frej Barty, Grade 9
Mendocino High School, Mendocino County
Sam Stump, Classroom Teacher
Blake More, Poet-Teacher

The Way We Change

The way we change,
Oh the way we change,
Have you realized how sick we are,
Selfish, not caring?
Our planet is dying
But no one seems to care.
Our people, animals, LIFE!
Where, where is it going?
Like a big dark hole,
Pulling us in
But we must, must fight back.
We're only living
In an ugly frame these days.
Let's try to change,
I wanna get out of
This ugly frame.

Stella Hughes, Grade 6
Coastal Grove Charter School, Humboldt County
Shana Langer, Classroom Teacher
Julie Hochfeld, Poet-Teacher

The Hill of Trash We Climb

after Amanda Gorman

We look up to the sky
and try to see through the smoke.

We're reaching for the stars
but all we can touch are neon lights.

We look down valleys and up mountains
to try to see the earth
but all we can see is trash.

We're diving for fish
but all we see is plastic.

We're digging for dinosaurs
but we only find dead machines.

The seas are spilling plastic,
the earth is burning from factories.

So we look inside our hearts for hope
but that light is fueled by coal.

Abi Bishop, Grade 7
Coastal Grove Charter School, Humboldt County
Clark Janklo, Classroom Teacher
Julie Hochfeld, Poet-Teacher

The Flames of Fire

You see an ember in the distance
That ember turns into a spark
The spark turns into a flicker of a flame
The flame grows, consuming EVERYTHING
You see the heat waves and hear a crackle
You can see orange, red, white...
The white is suffocating
The fire is always hungry for more
The smoke... the ash...
Makes it all worse
The circle of flame is humming, crackling
All-consuming
Ever hungry
All until it's put out by your hope
Your hope to live
Your hope to be
Your hope grows like the fire
Like the fire in your eyes and soul
Be confident
Be the fire
Consuming your doubt
Consuming your fear
Use it to fuel your creativity

Jenevieve Shaw, Grade 5
Oak Grove Elementary, Sonoma County
Debra Leonard, Classroom Teacher
Brennan DeFrisco, Poet-Teacher

Red Canna

after Georgia O'Keefe

I.

Red Canna,
red as burning hot fire
smooth as newborn
green leaves on a tree

II.

Inside the Red Canna is a meadow of stories
Inside that meadow of stories is a growing sun
Inside that growing sun is a universe of stories
I am the Red Canna learning in the sunrise
My anthers are soft like the flowing river

Michelle Chen, Grade 3
Francis Scott Key Elementary School, San Francisco County
Bonnie Rose Quinn, Classroom Teacher
Susan Terence, Poet-Teacher

I Blame The Water For Thinking It's Too Good

I'm from Florida, the home of the gators.

I'm from Florida, where your neighborhood
can get rough from time to time.

The home where all the people around
love oranges.

From the home where your ancestors
think the rules they grew up on
apply to you.

A wise man can play a fool,
but a fool can't play wise.

Keyondre Hargrove, Grade 12
Dewey Academy High School, Alameda County
Alea Luken, Classroom Teacher
Brennan DeFrisco, Poet-Teacher

There is a Place

Beyond the city choked in smoke,
with blaring horns
screaming through the day and night,
there is a place where the grass grows green,
a place where little birds sing as the trees sway in the breeze,
where the salmon swim in the streams,
and within this place there is a tree strong and tall,
always giving shelter to the small,
beyond the city choked in smoke,
with blaring horns screaming through the night,
there is a place.

Jonah Leo Veerkamp, Grade 4
Coastal Grove Charter School, Humboldt County
Marjorie Bertsch, Classroom Teacher
Julie Hochfeld, Poet-Teacher

Where I Am From

I am from where you hear a palotero
and everyone goes running to get an Elote

From a place where you hear, ¿Que Dios te Bendiga Mija?

I am from a place where you hear, Ya levantate es Hora de Misa

From a place where you are expected
to start cleaning and cooking from a young age

I am from a place where your parents
are up at 4:00 in the morning,
ready to pick some lemons

I am from a place where people are proud to be Brown

From a place called Santa Paula

Vanessa Galindo, Grade 11
Santa Paula High School, Ventura County
Nicola Lamb, Classroom Teacher
Fernando Albert Salinas, Poet-Teacher

Starry Night

after Vincent Van Gogh

The sky is as dark as the bottom of the sea
The wind howls like a wolf at midnight
The air as cold as the Arctic Ocean
Yet bright stars of glistening gold
fill the pitch-black sky with hope and beauty.
A small dark tree trunk sits on the ground
The tree is as dark as a black hole and is
Lifeless like a squashed roly-poly.
Yet around the dark lifeless tree
emerald green plants flourish.
The small town is filled with a warm hope
even if the wind howls like a wolf
even if it is as dark as the bottom of the sea
even if it is as cold as the Arctic Ocean,
the town will always have hope.
Nature has hope, even if plants are dry
as stone and lifeless like a puppet,
life will always flourish around it.
They both will always have hope because
they both know that
even in pitch-black darkness,
light will always follow.

Chinh Truong, Grade 7
Bonita Vista Middle School, San Diego County
Katherine Kavouklis, Classroom Teacher
Jonnierenee Nia Nelson, Poet-Teacher

Ukraine

War is the anger
that rips us apart.
Bombs break our peace.
Full range missiles
strike fear in our hearts.
Bullets pierce our hope.
But not our confidence.

Miles Lewis, Grade 2
Malcolm X Elementary, Alameda County
Kathryn C. Maps, Classroom Teacher
Maureen Hurley, Poet-Teacher

Haiku Collection

A howl is released
Intuition is ruthless
Shame on the full moon

A droplet of dew
New designs of life begin
Colored parasols

Thunder claps and cries
Nature's tears in every drop
When will this night end?

A wave of sand roars
Crashes in the desert plains
Gone, soon as it came

Pinwheels are in bloom
Bursting in the atmosphere
Happiness has grown

Ryan Alexander, Grade 6
Mill Valley Middle School, Marin County
Bethany Bloomston, Classroom Teacher
Michele Rivers, Poet-Teacher

Cold Christmas Eve

Steaming
hot chocolate
   frothy and
      bubbling
      marshmallows bobbing
             in the
               brown
                 lake
             sugar gently
               falling
             outside
             the frosted window
The Christmas tree   holding   sparkling
                          stars
    glittery orbs and   sweet candy
      sky as dark as
               tar
      and fire
         as warm as   lava
    the plush chair
      the Christmas voices
     gently humming
on a cold Christmas Eve

Catherine Zhao, Grade 5
Park School, Marin County
Danny Marsh, Classroom Teacher
Claire Blotter, Poet-Teacher

Five Haiku

Mist of secret truths
Walking with ghosts together
We reach through the trees

I stand in the snow
I watch the footsteps appear
Invisible love

Softly falling hail
Harshly falling rain of life
I am running wind

Drip drop waterfall
Liquid staircase of the falls
Reflecting my face

Tales of honeydew
Breeze and birds everything sweet
Sugar fairy lights

Eloise Lenehan, Grade 6
Mill Valley Middle School, Marin County
Bethany Bloomston, Classroom Teacher
Michele Rivers, Poet-Teacher

It Just Takes Time

I am a smooth serpentine pebble on Parsons Beach
Lying among millions of others
Polished by the waves crashing on the shore
The waves engulf me and pull me under like a wave of emotion

I am the resilient green kelp waving in the water
Not letting the current pull me away into the ultramarine abyss

I am the cool, deep blue water
Lapping the shore as the wind and tide push me
Filled with vibrant life

I am the endless cerulean blue sky
Painted with wispy clouds as soft as cotton candy
Casting a serene reflection on the surface of the water

I am the blinding golden sun
Shimmering and glistening on the water
Cheery light shattering on the ripples of the water

I am the silty tan sand
Warmed by the beaming rays of the sun
Like a warm blanket over the earth

But am I as confident as the steep cliffs surrounding me?
Maybe not now
Maybe in the near future
Maybe it just takes time
Takes time like how it takes time for a rock

To be polished into a pebble
And a pebble to slowly turn into soft, silty sand

Mayumi Takeda, Grade 9
Lowell High School, San Francisco County
Kristen Mitchell, Classroom Teacher
Susan Terence, Poet-Teacher

Lake Basin in the High Sierra

after Chiura Obata

Day full of angry thorns
Sitting along the plentiful gray rocks near the lake
Touching the prickly surfaces
Listening to silence
Breathing in clean air

I was the colorful rocks within the field of gray, old rocks
I was the tiny gems hidden within the rough and brown
      mountains
I was the joyful parasite that jumps around in the clear, calm
      waters
I have become the white ice sheets that melts into fresh, clear
water when the sun comes up

Looking down,
Dark blue as a whale
Smooth, glowing Sapphire water
Still like a lonely group of Hyacinths
Swayed by the tiniest wind
Ripples form with just a dust
Little life under the seas
Like the Lut Desert where no life lives

Looking straight ahead,
Mountain of shy orca whales
Sturdy as diamonds
Wanting to hide under the white blankets

Looking up,
Blackberry skies
No shooting stars
No glowing moon
No tiny gems
Just gray crying clouds
Sorrowful yet angry
As if a red wildfire started nearby
The universe has disappeared

Daena Lim, Grade 9
Lowell High School, San Francisco County
Sam Williams, Classroom Teacher
Susan Terence, Poet-Teacher

Starry Night

after Vincent van Gogh

We've never seen the ocean
This little town is too far from it
We imagine it was captured like the sky
By a creature with one ear and two eyes
I imagine the ocean like the wind
The constant flow and wave of it
Sunlight reflecting on the water
As the moon does on our smooth hills
I wouldn't mind the brightness of the ocean
After living in a town filled with blues
We blow out our lights and dream
Of the vastness of the world
Contrary to our small picture that we live in
It's quiet here
The constant church bells
Keep me awake
But they are too methodic
Too structured to
Keep me alive
There are no shells for my ears to peep into
Leaving the sound of the ocean entirely up
to my imagination
Like my mother saying
"Shhhhhh"
Before leaving us to our beds
In our little town

It's all very predictable
The ocean taunts me
Taunts us
With its incalculable movements
Its crashes and swishes of the sand
So fine it could slip through the smallest of cracks
I will see it someday
Feel it someday
I will escape this too-perfect little world of ours
And explore what you have kept from me

Adrienne Nguyen, Grade 9
Lowell High School, San Francisco County
Christian Villanueva, Classroom Teacher
Susan Terence, Poet-Teacher

The Wilderness In Me

What It Taught Me

What it taught me—

The deer, brave and bold,
taught me how to run like the wind
in the forest.

The calm willow tree
taught the scarred meadow
how to soar in the valley in the morning.

The lonely moon has secrets to tell you:
Even in the dark you are not alone.

In the poem of myself
I hear voices. I see what I never saw.
I feel the world.

Evie Moggio, Grade 3
Francis Scott Key Elementary School, San Francisco County
Bonnie Rose Quinn, Classroom Teacher
Susan Terence, Poet Teacher

I Believe In The Forest

I believe in the sound of the creek
I believe in the forest tree canopy
I believe in the flower petals on the ground,
    that surround me into a circle
I believe in the deer and rabbits, the birds and squirrels
I believe in the sunlight shining onto me
I believe in the souls of the ghosts of the forest
I believe in the green grass
I believe in the tree bark as a home of termites
I believe in the blue sky filled with rainbows
I believe in the sound of birds singing me a lullaby
I believe in the soft feeling of dirt
    on the tips of my toes
I believe in the pine trees, the oak trees,
the birch trees, the unknown
trees that live and give us oxygen
I believe in the beauty of the forest,
    because the forest
               is
                  beauty

Maxwelle Orr, Grade 6
Cuddeback School, Humboldt County
Cori Borges, Classroom Teacher
Dan Zev Levinson, Poet-Teacher

Ode to Trees

Oh, trees
Oh, graceful green giants
Do you know of your dying relatives, of the few that have survived?
Have you ever thought about how it is to walk?
You are beautiful and amazing.
You are the looking glass to another world; a place to hide.
You smell like sap and walks in the woods.
You look like a perfectly imperfect jumble of life.
You taste like maple syrup and pancakes.
You feel like a rough rock under my hand.
You sound like a swish of the wind
as it brushes through your leaves and branches.
Thank you for giving me shade.

Grant Montagnino, Grade 5
Manchester Elementary, Mendocino County
Avis Anderson, Classroom Teacher
Blake More, Poet-Teacher

Under the Apricot Tree

Under
     the apricot tree
           leaves f
             al
              li
                ng

  wind,   come dance with me
waltz with the leaves   up and
                down up

and
    down
        bunch the
        leaves
        together

leap d
    o
     w
      n   into the depths

of the fa
     ll
       ing leaves whoosh

  the wind howling
a dog   begging to play
  orange   yellow   red   blursintoalight

the rays shining
           do
              wn on me

what fun
       un
         der the
           apricot
           tree

Abigail Chan, Grade 5
Park School, Marin County
Danny Marsh, Classroom Teacher
Claire Blotter, Poet-Teacher

The Apple in the Tree

The apple hangs in a tree   tree
Shaking in the breeze   tree
About to fall   tree tree tree
BAM! | tree
    Is | tree
      Falling | tree
        Falling | tree
      In |
        The |
          Breeze |
        The |
          Apple
           Has
            Fallen
             From
              The
              Tree

You must be saying "what is happening here?"
Well, when it said, *Bam!* the apple hit the floor
and broke the poem.
Sorry it broke, it's the tree's fault—not mine!

Kyle Huffman, Grade 6
Kid Street Learning Center, Sonoma County
Erin Fightmaster, Classroom Teacher
Sandra Anfang, Poet-Teacher

An Abandoned Apple

You are as green as the beautiful lily pads outside
As circular as the center comets in the comical universe
Every child yearns for your taste
Every bite brings a sweet and crunchy flavor
You come in many different shapes and sizes
Whether as small as the mouse hiding in the floorboards
Or as large as a jovial jade jewel
You are the sound of the calm after the storm
As bittersweet as the aroma of a wilted rose
You hide in the back of my refrigerator
Wanting to be seen
Wanting to be savoured
Wanting to be devoured
But instead
You turn out sour

Alyssa Farrelly, Grade 9
Lowell High School, San Francisco County
Kristen Mitchell, Classroom Teacher
Susan Terence, Poet-Teacher

The Earth Can Change

The earth can change.
Smoke comes out of the forest.
The ocean turns to stone.
Waterfalls stop.
People die.
Animals are gone.
The earth can change.

Iris Thompson, Grade 3
Trillium Charter School, Humboldt County
Katie Dens, Classroom Teacher
Dan Zev Levinson, Poet-Teacher

Plastic Rain

Note to future self:
Rain is filled with plastic.
Willows won't wilt, redwoods will thrive.
Rivers will rush, the fish will survive.
If only and only if you don't pollute.
Kids will run.
People will have fun.
Covid will go.
No more need to lay low.

Kate Early, Grade 5
Skyfish School, Humboldt County
Pete Harrison, Classroom Teacher
Dan Zev Levinson, Poet-Teacher

The Ocean's Hands

The ocean's hands shape the earth,
crashing upon the shores,
tides going in and out,
these hands are waves,
floating on the top of the water,
waiting to strike.

These hands have created rivers,
and buried mountains,
they have moved boulders,
and made beaches.

Now, they are crying out for help,
as vile objects float through their waters,
as oil drips into the deep, dark water,
the coral reefs are destroyed by global warming,
Now, they need our help.

Norah Souza, Grade 4
Hydesville Elementary, Humboldt County
Alison Sturdevant, Classroom Teacher
Dan Zev Levinson, Poet-Teacher

Smoke

I smell smoke billowing in the distance
I see red in the sky
Why?
I'll tell you why...
The planet is heating
Carbon and the atmosphere are quite often meeting
I get a feeling that my chest will explode
It's all that smoke in my lungs
I can feel it on my tongue
My house is gone
Buried in a pile of ash
I'm starting to crash
I still will not last
My heart is no longer beating fast
In fact, it isn't beating at all
I've answered the call
Now I'm slowly walking to the other side
My life no longer abides in the vine
This light of mine is out of time
Whoosh
It went out
The smoke pours from my mouth
I'm still choking on the smoke on the other side
It followed me
And now it has swallowed me

Ethan LoCicero, Grade 9
Alder Grove Charter School, Humboldt County
Julie Hochfeld, Classroom Teacher & Poet-Teacher

How To Be A Rainforest

a cento by 2ⁿᵈ grade students

Study the leopards and sloths climbing your bark
Be friends with snakes and frogs on your forest floor
Look for rain drops dripping through your overstory
Hear the jaguars' growl and the toucans' squawking
Remember the snakes swinging from vine to vine in the Amazon
Eat the sweet, delectable fruit from the trees
Be friends with the baby sloth getting nice and warm with its
    mother
Hear the birds chirping and calling in the tall, tall trees
Feel snakes gliding on your branches
Laugh at the howler monkeys swinging in your trees
Forget the wildfires and sawing tree cutters
Catch up to a leaping jaguar hidden in the shadows
Enjoy the colorful flowers that pop out on the Kapok tree.
Visit the river rushing through the wind
Breathe in the humid air
Teach the scientists who study you
Be glad you are still here
Always share your love and happiness with the EARTH

Classroom Students, Grade 2
Montecito Elementary School, Santa Barbara County
Judy Compton, Heidi Craine, Brighton Judy, Classroom Teachers
Lois Klein, Poet-Teacher

Snow Creation

It is the soft and hard rock
that is frozen from the moon
The magical dreams of God falling onto Earth
Mother Nature saving dying plants from heat
It's the cherry on top of the ice cream of winter
Angels dropping water from the sky
And it turns into snow,
Earth's birthday present.

Cru Stirman, Grade 4
Park School, Marin County
Leslie Bernstein, Classroom Teacher
Claire Blotter, Poet-Teacher

Spring

I believe spring is the time of youth
Where the whole world somehow
Every year seems new.
Spring is not the prologue to summer
Where the self-conscious teenager
Shall look in the mirror and point out her flaws.
No, spring is new beginnings
Where the youth becomes adults
As they cross the stage.
Leaving behind childhood imagination
In a way, begging for time to slow
And to speed
Where they leave the known world
For the unknown.
And acknowledge that small towns hold an impasse
And impasse in time
That when you come back twenty years from now
Nothing has changed.
Except for the new graying at your mother's temples
Or that you don't know the faces
In the sports column of your local Paper
But it is also love.
The love and fear of prom dates
The expectations, the shaking hand, and the quivering voice
The stomp of the heels and the drag of your dress
And the closeness of the one holding you
To the silly song of youth.
And you swear that this moment shall last

Caught up in a foolish time of love
With hopes, it'll last past summer
And hopes that it won't
It is getting married after college
When the whole world seems to have settled down
And the love of your then life is looking you in the eye.
In your parent's orchard
Where the blossoms have sprung
And the once puppy has grown old
With the shadow casting upon.
It is the birth of your first child
And its life
That you hold for that bittersweet impasse of time.
It is your children returning to that same small town
Where nothing yet everything has changed,
Including your new look of gray.

Sidney Regelbrugge, Grade 10
Youth Poet Laureate of Mendocino County
Point Arena High School, Mendocino County
Blake More, Poet-Teacher

Luminescent Meadow

The luminescent meadow taught me
how to smile in the spring.
The blue morning glory taught
the glistening hummingbird how to
fly in the warm summer breeze.

The sparkling sun has secrets to tell you.
Feeling alone? Guess what?
I'm alone every day
and I still shine.

In the song of myself,
I hear quiet fire.
I see a sunset.
I feel calm.

Katelyn Dang, Grade 3
Francis Scott Key Elementary School, San Francisco County
Sarah Chan, Classroom Teacher
Susan Terence, Poet-Teacher

A Beautiful Sky

It's a picture
It looks like an ocean, blue sky
It has clouds that are big and fluffy like a pancake
When the rain falls down from the sky
It's like the gods are pouring syrup

Ava Irwin, Grade 5
Fair Oaks School, Los Angeles County
Ericka Irwin, Classroom Teacher
Alice Pero, Poet-Teacher

Sun & Stars

The sun comes
from the people holding flashlights
high in the sky
making sunbeams
through your own window
Shooting stars are people running
with bright clothes
to explore the universe

Eli Warren, Grade 6
Fair Oaks School, Los Angeles County
Ericka Irwin, Classroom Teacher
Alice Pero, Poet-Teacher

About the Rain

The rain stopped to listen to music
And the rain heard music
It was outside near a train station
The rain, could it follow?
The rain cried to follow
And it couldn't because it was
across the ocean
And rain crossed over the ocean
He didn't know where the music
was coming from
He was lost
Then the song came to the rain

Zola Sakamoto-Morgan, Grade 1
Fair Oaks School, Los Angeles County
Shenan Sarkovich, Classroom Teacher
Alice Pero, Poet-Teacher

There Are Trees In The Hallway

there are trees in the hallway.
that's not a metaphor, there are manzanitas in between the e wing
and the f wing,
i stepped outside for a drink of water and there they were
with strange red-orange fruits blossoming in between the
buildings.

there is grass growing in the gutter,
over mr. oftedal's room.
it's taking root and taking back the d wing rooftops.

   i was driving through the desert
     in a rainstorm with my mother
       and she was rattling off ravines of worries
        and speaking skid marks of worst-case scenarios
         as we rattled through the canyon

          but i was thinking
           "look how much nature doesn't need us"

      so much has been said about "save the wilderness"
        and "protect the polar ice caps"

      but we are not her rescuer

That smokestack-oil-rig-mineshaft-polluted-water-turning-black
            is the way we poke the bear

          We insist on biting the hand that feeds,

but our Goldilocks Planet is turning her paw against us

we cannot keep choosing the losing side.

There are fruit trees in the hallways
and grass in the gutter
and there will be life on earth with or without us

She crawls in under the back door and colonizes countertops
and clambers up through cracks in the pavement
and despite treating Nature like a guest in her own home,
She is here.

She will always be here.

I'm standing in the doorway looking at a manzanita tree
and I'm thinking grim thoughts and writing sad things
but when I look at those red-orange berries I am not sad

The earth is a good and wonderful thing.

Madeline Miller
Youth Poet Laureate of Santa Barbara County

The Sycamore Tree

Once there was a sycamore tree.
The smooth trunk was like a seal's soft skin.
The skinny branches were like chicken's feet.
The huge leaves were like the mane of a lion just green.
And the whole tree, to me, is like half the Earth.

Liv Sarkovitz, Grade 3
Fair Oaks School, Los Angeles County
Ericka Irwin, Classroom Teacher
Alice Pero, Poet-Teacher

Animals

I have a hedgehog in me ... the round body that makes the predators hungry ... the black shiny eyes that makes everyone think I am weak ... the needles along my back that I normally hide the dark side of myself which could slaughter the ones that hunt my life.

I have a panda in me ... the big body that makes me lazy ... an irresistible attitude to food that can never be disturbed – holding the bamboo is the happiest time that I have.

I have a bat in me ... the black body that keeps me hidden in the dark ... the wings that keep me lifted in the midnight ... the outstanding ears that help me navigate where I should go ... the eyes that are useless in the dark ... the feeling that I can never find light.

I have a cat in me ... the light body that swifts in the air and snatches the prey I targeted ... the brain that quickly changes its mind ... the eyes that give me sight in the dark – the eyes that give me hope - the eyes that make me think I can go through anything.

I have a lion in me ... the cleverness used in hunting ... the roar that scares off everything it is against ... the strict rules that make the woman hunt and the man protect ... the love for its child to make them the king of the animals.

I have a fox in me ... the beautiful ones that have nine fabulous tales ... the wisdom that helps me know what is right ...

sometimes is beautiful and sometimes a monster ... sometimes
shows its sharp fangs and protects what she thinks is right.

All of the animals in me, make up who I am.
None of them can disappear
or that just wouldn't be me.

Sae Tsutsui, Grade 5
Strawberry Point School, Marin County
Rachel Quek, Classroom Teacher
Terri Glass, Poet-Teacher

The Wilderness In Me

There is a pufferfish inside me.
It inflates with its strong poison and spikes.
From it, I learned to defend myself.

There is a wasp inside me.
It can sting anything and everything infinitely.
The wilderness gave this to me as a gift of flight.

There is a bighorn sheep inside me.
With its ramming horns, it can face the biggest challenge.
The wilderness gave this to me as a gift of protection.

Kalani Douglas, Grade 4
Mountain View Elementary, Santa Barbara County
Katherine James, Classroom Teacher
Cie Gumucio, Poet-Teacher

Raccoon

Black masked bandit
SCRATCH BAM
Thief SLAMS cooler lid
sneaking into the night
backyard's BIGGEST problem
comfort in shadow
Hot Dog STOLEN!
SUCH a bandit

Sophia Roberts, Grade 4
Montecito Union School, Santa Barbara County
Megan Soderborg, Classroom Teacher
Cie Gumucio, Poet-Teacher

The Phoenix of Fire

I am the phoenix of fire.
From the winds I learn to fly like the clouds of time.
I taught the wolf to howl at the moon.
I dream of peace in the world.

Patrick Robinson, Grade 2
Alexander Valley School, Sonoma County
Sarah Sheehy, Classroom Teacher
Maureen Hurley, Poet-Teacher

I Am

I am a bear in a forest hunting for food.
I am a leaf ready to fall off the tree.
I am a bird flying through the air from branch to branch.
I am a spirit remembering the places I've been.
I am a fish in the water feeling as if I was flying.
I am a dandelion letting my offsprings fly off me to grow a new
     generation.
I am a tree doing nothing but bending with the route of the wind.
I am a raindrop falling fast and then landing on the tip of the
     grass.
I am a volcano alive.
I stand with great joy.
I can be calm.
I can be calm.

Hayden Coate, Grade 3
Mountain View Elementary, Santa Barbara County
Pia Tsuruda, Classroom Teacher
Cie Gumucio, Poet-Teacher

Ode to My Dog

Oh, Kona, your fur is like the softest sheep's wool.
It is so soft, it's practically like petting clouds,
and the color, oh your color looks like sunlight
on a shining forest fire.

Your eyes are like the trunk of a redwood in a forest glade,
a beautiful brown. They look into my soul trying
to solve my problems.

Your nose is like the ink that comes out of a pen,
it sniffs out my tears trying to scare them away.
When I snuggle with you, you are worth more
then all the jewels, treasures and riches of the world.

I love you and I know you love me when you sleep
on my bed filling the emptiness that was once there.
You are the best dog in the world- the gentlest, kindest and cutest.

Your personality is outstanding- peaceful and quiet,
sometimes energetic and adventurous.
Either way, you are the key to my happiness.
You will always have a place in my heart.

Maya Livingston, Grade 3
Old Mill School, Marin County
Graham Davis, Classroom Teacher
Terri Glass, Poet-Teacher

Oly

Big-bone chewer.
Really loved licking.
Super great fetcher.
Protector of the house.
Hated any skateboard.
Except for when I was riding.
Loved going on runs.
Ate only when we ate.
Marvel-movie watcher.
Watched his first and last with us.
Wiley asked to see him.
He wasn't breathing.
My mom wasn't home.
We took him to the vet.
Ashes he will come back as.
Spread in the places he loved.
Will always still be here.
In our hearts.
He died in peace.
Knew me like the back of his paw.
Always answered the door.
Barked when it wasn't us.
I never had to worry.
Because he was right there.
Until now.
Now he is in our hearts.
Loved forever and ever.

Felix W. Felsenthal, Grade 4
Coastal Grove Charter School, Humboldt County
Marjorie Bertsch, Classroom Teacher
Julie Hochfeld, Poet-Teacher

My Heart

My heart is a loyal, yet independent cat
It has sleek silky fur, and a rumbling, contented purr
It wants to sprint after its favorite toy, paws skidding
on the hardwood floor
Then spend hours curled up in a cozy corner
Safe
Most of time, it is a friendly, albeit strong spirited kitten
Ears twitching
Tail swishing from side to side
But sometimes, out from its velvety paws
slide needles of razor-sharp anger
And its purr sputters out
Replaced by a threatening growl
It slinks off to a dark secluded place,
contemplating revenge
But after a while, it can't help but get up
Stretch
And look around
What fun is this
Skulking about
It just wants to chase shadows and tussle with its friends,
be the perky kitten after all

Béla Randles, Grade 7
Coastal Grove Charter School, Humboldt County
Clark Janklo, Classroom Teacher
Julie Hochfeld, Poet-Teacher

On the Other Side of the Moon

On the other side of the moon, there are star clusters making different shapes and colors that anyone can see as something.

On the other side of the moon, there are comets, asteroids, and meteors flying around through the pitch-black darkness like it's butter.

On the other side of the moon, planets circle around the blazing sun like they're her servants, trapped in orbit forever, until the blazing sun queen dies.

Clara Rudnicki, Grade 3
Montecito Union School, Santa Barbara County
Lisa Monson, Classroom Teacher
Kimbrough Ernest, Poet-Teacher

The Moon and Stars

My poem is like the moon and stars in my heart.
My brother is like a horse galloping on the sand
and as the sand turns black,
the flames come together, galloping in the night.
My parents shine as bright as the sun.
My brother is like the moon and the stars.
My grandparents are like horses galloping on the sand.
And we are like the constellations
shining in the night sky.

Joaquin Reisman, Grade 2
Malcolm X Elementary, Alameda County
Jila Abdolhosseini & Jessica Arroyo, Classroom Teachers
Maureen Hurley, Poet-Teacher

My True Name

If my eyes could speak, they would tell
about the stars in the universe.
My voice is water gushing out of my mouth.
There is a star in my brain wanting to see
things that it has never seen before.
There is a place inside my soul,
it is a tree lit with candles.
My true name is made of stars.

Zachary Hess, Grade 3
Park Elementary School, Marin County
Julie Herrera, Classroom Teacher
Maureen Hurley, Poet-Teacher

Memories Rushing By

Grandma

My heart is the flickering flame on the stove
A comforting warm on a cold day
When I look at her

Her tanned wrinkled hands
Softly knead the powdered white dough
She takes a piece of it and carefully molds it into a disc
The way she treats the dough is like how someone handles a
    newborn
The thought of how she has loved me rises in my head like a
    balloon
filled with care and compassion

Her smile is the warm yellow glow of a lantern in the night
When she hands me the newly flattened circle
To fill with the light pink raw meat mixed with all sorts of spices
    and vegetables
A clump in the center
I fold the circle in half, closing up the edge to seal my love letter
Then I carefully place it into the steamer, so it can cook

After it comes out of the pot of steam
The dumpling is a glass sculpture,
For it could break apart if dropped
When you first bite into it tastes like home
It is soft and warm
The perfect picture of what my grandma is

My grandma is beautiful
She is the sun on a rainy day
The gentle stream in the valley
On a warm spring afternoon

Jessica Tam, Grade 9
Lowell High, San Francisco County
Alison Kent, Classroom Teacher
Susan Terence, Poet Teacher

My Great-Grandmother as a Business Owner

I smell of fresh, baby blue detergent
Soapy and clean
Shiny and new
Bubbly like the daily customers who signal the familiar chime
of the rusted golden bell above the old oak tree door
They cradle their laundry in their arms
    as if it's a delicate newborn
Every day I sit and watch the cars passing by
    on the street out front
Like watching the same tv show on repeat
The same cars pass daily for their morning commute,
    then followed by their home commute
My daily soundtrack of honking and screeching mixed with
the sounds of zippers clashing with the metal inside the spinning
    washing machines
The ticking from the turning dials of the machines signifying that
    the wash is done
The buzzing from the static of the dryers running
The splashes of flowing water as the machines are filled with it
The clanking of dirty copper, nickel, and zinc coins being inserted
    into the "pay here" slot
My hair constantly frizzy from the humid,
sticky air that filled the space day after day
But at the end of the day,
I am the proud business owner of this laundromat
that is arguably my second home

Ashley Young, Grade 9
Lowell High School, San Francisco County
Chad Gaver, Classroom Teacher
Susan Terence, Poet-Teacher

Errand Boy

written in the voice of an ancestor

The people in town
Know me as the errand boy
I deliver what needs to be delivered
Say what needs to be said
Think what needs to be thought
Do what needs to be done

I wait by the corner
Newspaper in hand
Throat dry and sore
I make fair trades that day
I'll continue again tomorrow

My feet are burning
My back is sore
The weight of the pail
Feels like I'm carrying the entire town
Golden hair glows in the sun
Her ocean eyes
The treasure of the small town
If only the waves would crash towards me

I am simply a boy
A boy of many uses
Many talents
In a small town

Use me as you see fit
For I have no ambition
But to leave this small world
And explore an even bigger one

Sydney Sullivan, Grade 9
Lowell High School, San Francisco County
Angelina Cowan-Byrns, Classroom Teacher
Susan Terence, Poet-Teacher

Lubava Sosnovskaya

I come from Russia
I am the daughter of a woman who doesn't know war
A woman who knits happily sitting in her chair
I'm a daughter of a man who's never held a bloody sword
A married woman with a son
Suddenly a war hit and everything changed
I went off to be a nurse
My husband went to fight
My beautiful brown locks turned into flimsy straws
And the innocent smile turned into a saddened frown
And when the war is over
I was left with a souvenir of medals
When I came home, I was still a mother
But a widow nonetheless
I met a new man
Had two more children a son and a daughter
Later I moved to the Americas with my son and girl and my
grandchildren
Now I am a great grandmother
Quietly sitting watching out of a window
Withering away, for my good years are past me
97, older than the queen, but in no way do I intend to abdicate
Leave my story untold, I shall not.

Alexandra Sosnovskaya, Grade 9
Lowell High School, San Francisco County
Anne Torres, Classroom Teacher
Susan Terence, Poet-Teacher

Printing the Truth

Ida B. Wells was a typewriter for truth.
She was a pencil who erased racism.
Ida B. Wells was a pen printing
the truth about lynchings.
Sharp and courageous,
her writing was heroic to her people.
May her brave words soar
as fearlessly as a falcon.

Interview with Ida B Wells

My heart is like a river that flows
through a dream about justice for all.
No one can stop me.

Fumiko Peagler, Grade 2
Malcolm X Elementary, Alameda County
Dr. Kathryn Mapps, Classroom Teacher
Maureen Hurley, Poet-Teacher

Women Throughout Time

Mothers to their daughters:
Don't be too loud or proud
Bold nor uncontrolled
Can't react you'll only overreact
Bite your tongue
Keep quiet, you're just a girl
This is man's world
You're a simple muse, so follow the rules

Society to all the Muses:
We have a made an iron cage
engraved for the daughters of Zeus
We decided your role
We control the way you're supposed to
Act in our society
We've deemed you as the "weaker" sex

Men to women in society:
We are lords and you are our servers
Bring the bread and wine
Cook and clean
Put the kids to bed
I am your provider
Make sure I'm satisfied at the end
Remember, i chose you
Don't make me regret choosing you

Women in mirror:
We have been forced inside a box
Suffocating & humiliating
Told to bite our lip
Hold our tongue
Swallowed our dignity & pride
To overlook the gender pay gap
And the fact we have been forced into a lifetime
Of a written outline
Of bake sales and teatime,
A divine punchline
Since the beginning of all mankind

Jessica Dominguez, Grade 11
Oxnard Middle College High School, Ventura County
Jennifer Brickey, Classroom Teacher
Fernando Salinas, Poet-Teacher

Frida Kahlo

I didn't want to change myself
To meet people's expectations.
My unibrow made me feel confident and free
It felt like a fuzzy caterpillar
People might have thought I was weird
But it made me feel unique.
I felt like my heart was broken into a thousand pieces
Frail and depressed
I was furious with my sister most of all
But I did find it in my heart to forgive them
Forgiveness is such a beautiful thing.
I didn't always want to be an artist
But I was deeply inspired by indigenous Mexican culture
Bright and dramatic
I loved how I was free to express myself
I loved how the oily pastels felt in my hand
And how the canvasses felt so smooth.

Sofia Rodriguez, Grade 8
Bonita Vista Middle School, San Diego County
Katherine Kavouklis, Classroom Teacher
Johnnierenee Nia Nelson, Poet-Teacher

Lake Trip Shine

Floating fluidly, flames flick the fly.
On the lake trip shine, glitter skins the eye.
Long, not loud, living large light.
On the lake trip shine, can I see—I might.

The lake, clear as a window,
    reflecting stars on full moon night,
      any color like a rainbow smooshed on tight.
Calmly carries cliff, clean, sound.
Lake trip shine, all day around.

George Tyler, Grade 3
Montecito Union School, Santa Barbara County
Jacki Hammer, Classroom Teacher
Kimbrough Ernest, Poet-Teacher

Summer Vacation

Summer vacation,
Filled with the bluest waters,
Bluer than the color itself.
Staring at the books, the books on the shelf.
Telling myself how much I should read,
but I'm busy staring out at the sea.

Summer vacation,
A picnic at the park,
The dogs began to bark.
The yellowest ducks I've ever seen,
swimming down the crystal-clear water with the breeze.
As I feel the soft grass I begin to realize
how much I enjoy summer.

Summer vacation,
The days that pass,
The flowers that grow,
Your colorful sunsets,
And the beauty that you show.

Macie Olin, Grade 7
Lo-Inyo School, Inyo County
Bob Heist, Classroom Teacher
Fernando Salinas, Poet-Teacher

This Is Actually a Gum Commercial

Trident gum tastes like early Sunday mornings
My mother still wet here
The overpowering stench of my father's cologne
It feels like hunger and a quick bowl of cereal
Before admitting or giving my love to God

The stained glass in which I would lose myself
As the father continues the gospel
Well, my dad nudges me
What are the pages of the book
Well, the Bible
What should be so much better
If I could simply read it in one singular setting

My knee still bounces and padding was never enough
The relentless, prayers, promises,
and words embedded in my kneecaps
The same never-ending "Our Fathers"
I believe 15 more minutes after the
Peace be with you and Mary Alice's

Sweet, sweet, sugarcoated perfume
The potlucks are always announced
Yet we never attended one
We weren't that type of family

But a Diner's breakfast
A plate of hot, steaming really not that good biscuits and gravy

The change from Sunday Best to Sunday worst
Stain jeans and ripped tennis shoes
Snap goes Mother's gum.

Sidney Regelbrugge, Grade 10
Youth Poet Laureate of Mendocino County
Point Arena High School, Mendocino County
Blake More, Poet-Teacher

Mother

Who is from the lightest clouds.
Who calls me funny, crazy, lovely and smart.
Who tells me love is big and blind.
Who remembers to share the smallest day.
Whose eyes are the glittering green of an emerald.
In her I see the darkest rain of the lightest sky.
Whose hands are as soft as a sheep but as cold as a bad deed.
Who feeds me love and wonder.
Whose voice is louder than an elephant and softer than a
    heartbeat.
She is the loudest sound from the lightest touch.

Ella Blue Newby, Grade 3
Francis Scott Key Elementary School, San Francisco County
Katherine Johnson, Classroom Teacher
Susan Terence, Poet-Teacher

Someone You Loved

I believe friends are soul mates
The person is kind like the flowers
The person's style is like the sunsets
I will never forget the support I had
The person is half of me
The hugs are like clouds
We will grow together like trees
The person's smile is like the sharp blade
The person shines through the darkness
The person is beautiful, perfect, and amazing
I forget who I am around the person
The person's voice is like a beautiful musical
The person is like an adorable puppy.

Dakota Gomes, Grade 8
Rancho Santana School, San Benito County
Carly Obertello, Classroom Teacher
Amanda Chiado, Poet Teacher

Love Is Love

Strolling in the rain,
On a peaceful night
With my significant other.

His warm hugs make me happy
On the cold nights
We stand in the orange sunset
And dance our way into the night

It's always so calming
In the knowhere
Is where we are

His truck lights sparkling in the sunset
Makes the night just right
And the music
Will never get old.

Brooklyn Hettinger, Grade 8
Rancho Santana School, San Benito County
Carly Obertello, Classroom Teacher
Amanda Chiado, Poet Teacher

A Fading Memory

Her chin held high,
While looking at him,
Memories rushing by,
The sky became dim;

His eyes looked back,
In worry and sorrow,
Knowing that,
She'll never see tomorrow;

He held her to the sky,
As the wind blew by,
A kiss to the cheek,
His final goodbye.

Zack Miguel Paciente, Grade 8
Rancho Santana School, San Benito County
Carly Obertello, Classroom Teacher
Amanda Chiado, Poet-Teacher

The Dirt Nap

The dirt nap is long and dark
the only place that you can relax.
But when kids and familia come and start to party
it makes you want to party
You shoot up and watch them dance
singing and eating the finest bread mmm.
My mom and I had a good time as ghosts in the night.
We watch till the sunlight then go back down, down, down.
Mmm a delicious night!!
My mom's casserole is so good
but we are gone, so no more casserole for me.

Ta'coya 'Paris' Burrill, Grade 4
Kid Street Learning Center, Sonoma County
Melaine Curran, Classroom Teacher
Sandra Anfang, Poet-Teacher

My Polarized Home

I come from a humble home, rural and slow
My home is both I don't know the difference
India, Pakistan Bhai Bhai...
Why shall what we believe in matter?
Don't they love us no matter what?
The terror in my village, like hell on horses with spears
Grandma hid me in the hay bale, she saved me from death
I've known what now is two countries, as one sanctuary
Hindu Muslim Bhai Bhai...
The dirt paths, filled with bloody cloth and destroyed hope
The farms, OUR farms
Destroyed...burned to the ground like our hope of peace
The violence seems endless, the trains filled with "warriors"
The deceased warriors now...
The weather feels muggy and orange
Like someone murdered the sun
Just like how someone murdered our people
We pray it ends!
Prayers unanswered, just like the letters to our loved ones...

Arin Kumar, Grade 9
Lowell High School, San Francisco County
Angelina Cowen-Byrn, Classroom Teacher
Susan Terence, Poet-Teacher

How Lonely I Am

Imagining being held at Angel Island, a detention camp for immigrants from Asia from 1910-1940, where detained immigrants carved poems into the walls to express their feelings.

Outside, I see San Francisco, way in the distance.
I hear the birds chirping in the warm, sunny weather.
Aaahhh, how I wish I were the birds, flying, wandering around
and chirping. I wish I could see San Francisco
and not be stuck here in Angel Island!
Inside, I see dirty walls, the big room filled with
bunk beds. On each, three levels of beds.
I miss my home in a quiet village in China.
I remember my mom and my sisters that were left behind,
way back in China. I think it's more peaceful there than here.
I miss my mom and my sister.
I feel like I'm someone's prisoner, even though
I'm not a criminal, didn't do something wrong.
Being at Angel Island is like staying in jail.
Everywhere is black and dusty.
Everyone is carving into the walls with knives
how lonely they have been since they came to Angel Island.
I wish I could go to San Francisco.
But how will I ever get out of here?
I wish my mom and my sister were here.
Oh, how I wish I could wander around in the city with my family.
I miss my family so, so much, you can't even believe it.
I always cry before I go to bed.

Nargiza Fayzieva, Grade 3
Francis Scott Key Elementary School, San Francisco County
May Chung, Classroom Teacher
Susan Terence, Poet-Teacher

The Daring Grandfather

I run like the small, gray mice in the alleyways
glancing back to make sure we were not being followed.
My heart raced as if it were running with us
and was just as fearful of being caught.
The fog horns near the dock roared like lions as we got closer to
       them
and the smell of salt and the sight of water gave me hope
as I knew we were so close to our destination.
My father, the great, wise, red dragon
like those I knew from stories of ancient China,
who chose to take me rather than leave me behind with the rest
       of my family,
gave all the money he had on him to the ship worker,
and I saw the raw greed in his eyes
break the worker's strict loyalty he had to the Communist Party.
He gave us a nod and a smug smile, and we ran as fast as we
       could onto the boat.
We hid in the dark shadows of the cargo
and soon, we felt the boat moving away from the docks.
I am the piece of dead driftwood
floating aimlessly in the sea
knowing that one day
I will reach land.

Darren Lee, Grade 9
Lowell High School, San Francisco County
Angelina Cowen-Byrn, Classroom Teacher
Susan Terence, Poet-Teacher

Peiyu Chen De Gushi (Peiyu Chen's Story)

my voice rings clear across the water
the echoless expanse is lonely
i strain my ears to listen for a reply
the roll of the tides greets my call

i play with a stone weathered by the waves
languid hours with my feet in salt spray
such is the life of a vagabond
(when was stone replaced with jewel?)
(downturned lips painted red?)
(a bridal veil covering tear tracks?)

someone answers my verses
sun scorches fire on my cheeks
i raise a hand to shield my eyes
choking ring absent from my left hand
(to keep it safe from being lost to the riptide, i say)
(i don't believe the lie, but he does)
siren songs on a distant shore
a mirage?
a trick of the heat?
but i hear it again

strong baritone carries well across the water
echoless may it be, but this expanse is empty no longer
hello stranger with a voice of silk and honey
sing me the stories you call home

are exchanges on the waterfront enough to call love?
is another man's ring on my finger just a fallacy?
trapped in a marriage devoid of love
i sing to the water
drown in his depths
take my hand, love
i watch the band of silver get swallowed by infinitesimal depths
it's time we turn our backs to the ocean
and voyage into the earth

Maggie Yu, Grade 9
Lowell High School, San Francisco County
Angelina Cowan-Byrns, Classroom Teacher
Susan Terence, Poet-Teacher

Papo Ital's Grand Escape

It is midnight and I am
held captive in a room
surrounded by a flag of red and white

My hands are clasped together
a prayer leaves my lips
Iligtas mo ako, I repeat over and over
like a mantra

When I am out on the veranda
I am alone
and I plan my final attempt to escape

The sky is an empty void
darkness swallows the trees
and I cannot see the pointed fences that enclose the area
like a death trap for fools

But I jump
a leap of faith
and land on the other side

The tense night air carries rough shouts and quick footsteps
but my feet, my blood, my heart
pulse quicker
and the soldiers do not catch me

I run to where the mangroves line the riverbank
and I let the inky waters envelop me

My arms are sore
and the taste of gritty clam
lingers in my mouth
from countless days and nights
swimming through the river
but I push on
A kind face finds me at the end of the river
he guides me back to my village
Suddenly the skies are clearer and the sun glows brighter
and my heart, though it aches,
swells with hope

It is morning and I am
home again

Jadel Cristobal, Grade 9
Lowell High School, San Francisco County
Christian Villanueva, Classroom Teacher
Susan Terence, Poet-Teacher

Papo – Sambal for "Grandparent"
Iligtas mo ako – Tagalog for "Save me"

My Scope of Imagination

A Moment In Time

I am a single flickering lamp post lighting up a dark alleyway,
Before it gives in and darkness hurrahs,
I am the smell in the air just before it rains,
The crisp gust of wind that nips at your ear
During a late, foggy, bitterly cold night in San Francisco

I am the wick of a melting candle
I am the moment just before the dancing fire snuffs out,
Burnt and exhausted,
When the smoke is all that is left
Here I am still reaching and yearning for a spark of ember

My comrades say, "A coffee colored giraffe you are, towering
        over the Golden Gate Bridge"
One day I hope to be a gray cat – lazing away in the burning sun
        all day
I am a brown spotted banana that is sweetest just before it rots
I am the moment before bubbles pop
The memories you hold onto with an iron grip

I am the seconds between each minute on the clock
Tick, tick, tick, ticking away
I am not a celestial being, neither planet nor star
I cannot dance and attend parties with the sun and moon
For I am merely one fleeting single mortal, a speck of purple dust
The whole universe can play, and over time that iron grip will
loosen up

As the light had its final say,
As the fire gives its last bow,
As the seconds continue to tick away,
The memories will fade and all traces of me are wiped away
Funny isn't it,
How Time works?

Here I am, with a blink of an eye
and just a millisecond missed,
Like a thief I disappear,
For I am the moment before
and not a second later.

Sabrina Lee, Grade 9
Lowell High School, San Francisco County
Kristen Mitchell, Classroom Teacher
Susan Terence, Poet-Teacher

Patience Is A Thing

after Emily Dickinson

Patience is the thing with fur,
with a silent heart,
sleeps all day and only gets up
for a drink or food.
Little Kitty, as soft as a cloud.
She never touched water in her life.
She goes outside once a day.
Sometimes comes back in,
or never comes back at all.

Ainsley Kolodziejski, Grade 3
Park Elementary School, Marin County:
Julie Herrera Classroom Teacher
Maureen Hurley, Poet-Teacher

I Offer You Love

I offer you love

I offer you a warm blanket that will warm you in the cold.

I offer you my heart.

I offer you peace, joy, happiness, and love.

Love is all you will need.

I offer you my warmth and comfort.

I will offer you almost all of my joy.

I offer you my sorrows.

Remy Falcon Failes, Grade 2
Malcolm X Elementary School, Alameda County
Dr. Kathryn Mapps, Classroom Teacher
Maureen Hurley, Poet-Teacher

Sadness

I awoke in a house so bleak, it would have made anyone cringe.
The thing that caught my eye, a pitch-black humanoid figure
with stars all over his body.

He said,
I am your sadness, your anger,
I have always been there, watching.

I asked, *Then why do you choose to show yourself now, of all times?*

Because you are dead.

I shrieked and everything went black.

Jack Battuello, Grade 5
Oak Grove Elementary School, Sonoma County
Jonathan Devlin, Classroom Teacher
Brennan DeFrisco, Poet-Teacher

Black As Night

The heart is as black as night.
Life rolls over the lake of darkness.
Heart is as black as night.
It lies to friendship. No more of that.
Heart is as black as night.
It becomes a dragon of smoke and
flies over the window of darkness.
Heart is as black as night.
Heart buzzing with vines and bones,
it shifts into a ghost.
Heart is as black as night.
Crawling through pain and
bodies of death.
Heart is as black as night.
Heart is closed in and can't get out.
Heart is as black as night.
Waking up and happiness.
I guess it was all just a dream.
Heart is as black as night.

Sofia Lau, Grade 2
Malcolm X Elementary School, Alameda County
Dr. Kathryn Mapps, Classroom Teacher
Maureen Hurley, Poet-Teacher

Night & Day

Night and day,
They are chasing each other,
Endlessly full of energy,
But,
Who is chasing the other?
Is it Sun?
Bright, with a fiery passion.
Eyes that glow like lava.
She has white, red, orange, and yellow hair,
Shifting in the wind, flowing like fire.
Or is it Moon?
Sad, cold, ethereal, and calm.
Her hair covers her blue eyes that hold wisdom
The same hair blue, white, and gray, like a waterfall
Warmly glowing.
So who is chasing who?
Or did one just pull the other's hair?

Elora Wanden, Grade 6
Coastal Grove Charter School, Humboldt County
Shana Langer, Classroom Teacher
Julie Hochfield, Poet-Teacher

Inseparable Lyra and Daria

Lyra dances in the flowers,
a bright smile stretched across her lemon-colored face.
Her rosy, flecked cheeks puff up with joy
as she hums to the soft tune of small birds.

Daria sulks under the ground, filled with rage.
A wicked grumble plastered on her ash-colored face.
Her freckled cheeks puff up with anger
as she lays heavy on her throne.

Lyra kisses the wild horses,
and twirls on the vanilla-sanded beach.
She bites into strawberry shortcake
and throws a tea party with the bears and bees.

Daria sharpens her sword,
and struts across the halls made of granite
She gorges on meat, wine, and bread.
and throws a party with the dead.

Lyra and Daria are inseparable.
Light would not exist without darkness.
Darkness would not exist without the light.
One shows not a trace of harshness
and the other always fights.

Avani Padki, Grade 6
Mill Valley Middle School, Marin County
Bethany Bloomstron, Classroom Teacher
Michele Rivers, Poet-Teacher

Lyra – Lightness
Daria – Darkness

The Separation of Shades

Darkness slithers across the floor
of a musty library at night
He crawls between the pages
when Lightness calls for the day

Lightness strokes the bushes outside my window
She wakes up, asking me to awake too
She feels hurt when I close the shutters in the morning
knowing Darkness was chuckling inside

Darkness wraps around the bark of the pine tree
protecting the woodland creatures hiding in the leaves
They watch a human resting in the cool shade
beneath the sap-coated branches

Lightness watches from above
Sad that some had become bored of her on the beach
She ducks into a cloud
Frustrating those sunbathing on the sand

Darkness and Lightness meet at sunrise
They greet each other for the brand-new day
They also wave the mist away
To say goodnight at sunset

Once they had said their salutations
The world is at peace
For nothing is better
Than the ending of separate ways

Poppy Wintermute, Grade 6
Mill Valley Middle School, Marin County
Bethany Bloomston, Classroom Teacher
Michele Rivers, Poet-Teacher

The Other Half

When God said,
"Let there be light,"
He also created darkness.

When Yin and Yang
rose out of the chaos,
they remained in harmony.

One half, bright as the moon
the other half, dark as the night.

But we,
we put labels on things,
said that white
was pure, was beautiful, was good.
said that black
was defiled, was ugly, was bad.

Who said?
Who dared to make this distinction,
that there was white
and there was black,
that there was good
and there was bad,
that there was one
and there was the other –
in a world of blurry, bleary gray?
in a world that is always an I for an I,
but not always a truth for a truth?
Who says?

Harmony, self-harmony.
Not harm on you, harm on we.

Because the Yin and the Yang
can never be separated
within, or without

Because the dark side of the moon
and the brightest, fullest side we see
are the same, just 15 days apart

Because the color of my skin, and the color of your skin,
and the color of their skin, are the same –
illusions of light.

One half, dark as the moon
the other half, bright as the night.

Distinctly different, but
Why not form
one circle

Not of light, and not of dark
Not of halves, and not of wholes –

Where there is no such thing as
the other half.

Amy Liu, Grade 10
Developing Virtue Girls School, Mendocino County
Rianne Kravits, Classroom Teacher
Blake More, Poet-Teacher

Life and Death

Life is like the unpredictable ocean
It comes and goes as it pleases

Life and Death are opposites
One is beautiful, the other is horror
Amazing but scary

People do amazing things
What is it worth in the end?

The wealthy can't bring their money
The famous can't bring their fame or fans
What is it all worth in the end?

You meet amazing people
Some not too good
Do amazing things and live life to the fullest
As you should

Death is the sadness and despair in your heart
It's like not knowing what to do
How to survive or feel

It happens if you want it to or not
Everyone does one day or another
What is it all worth in the end?

Gracie Marquez, Grade 8
Rancho Santana School, San Benito County
Carly Obertello, Classroom Teacher
Amanda Chiado, Poet-Teacher

Oh, Gold

Oh, gold, Oh gold.
  You are the everlasting
    speed of the cheetah that
      fades into the foggy jungle
        depths. A single grain of sun
          reflecting sand left in my slippers.
            A magical pencil swaying back and
              Forth, and leaving its mark on the pale
                piece of paper that seems to be calling your
                  name, over the loud noises of birds singing
                    beautiful melodies and the rough sound of cars
                      slicing the road with their torn-up tires that have
                        Been through more than just cuts and scrapes on
                          the outside.

          Oh gold, Oh gold. Where have you gone?
                perhaps you

      have

      gone

      to

      the

      dark

      mysterious

caves

that

D
R
I
P

with

fear

that

you

the

bright

sun

will

E s c a p e   But I promise... I will find you.

Cash Lee, Grade 5
Montecito Union School, Santa Barbara County
Katie Nimitarnun, Classroom Teacher
Cie Gumucio, Poet-Teacher

Hope

Hope is the thing that happens
when you are waiting for a long, long time.

Hope is a spark in your brain
that explodes on the earth.

Hope feels like you are the most
powerful person in the world.

Ellie Berson, Grade 2
Malcolm X Elementary School, Alameda County
Dr. Kathryn Mapps, Classroom Teacher
Maureen Hurley, Poet-Teacher

Holding Everything

I woke up and felt nothing.
I looked to my hand and found everything.
I held dreams, filled with love and joy
that can warm the coldest night.
And sadness, which could freeze the warmest day.
It could tear down joy, it could destroy memories.
But most importantly, it was only a dream.

Noah Young, Grade 5
Oak Grove Elementary, Sonoma County
Jonathan Devlin, Classroom Teacher
Brennan DeFrisco, Poet-Teacher

Everything At Once

This is the color of a sunny sky.
This is the color of cotton candy at the fair.
This is the color of a daydream.
This is the color of victory, of triumph.
This is the color of a baby boy's blanket.
This is the color of peace and calm.
This is the color of meditation.
This is the color of returning home after an adventure.
But this is also a color of sadness.
This is the color of losing someone you love.
This is the color of drizzling rain.
This is the color of a long day.
This is the color of a sad song.
This is the color of a white lie.
This is the color of shyness.
This is the color of loneliness.
This is the color of whispers behind someone's back.
This is the color of everything at once.

Lillian Grace Maclay, Grade 5
Trinidad Elementary School, Humboldt County
Emmet Bowman, Classroom Teacher
Dan Zev Levinson, Poet-Teacher

Pink

I am the color pink.
My superpower is making the summer sunset.
When you are sad, I will become the stars
    that get to cheer you up.
When you are lost, I am the map to guide you home.
When you are confused, I will be the answer sheet
    to help you understand.
When you are lonely, I will be the night sky
    to keep you company.
When you are sick, I will be the medicine to help you get better.

I am the color pink, and I am your ink.

Wynne Singer, Grade 4
Montecito Union School, Santa Barbara County
Megan Soderborg, Classroom Teacher

Chartreuse

Chartreuse as the oak tree's fruit
Chartreuse as the ancient spring
Chartreuse as the turkey's flag of peace
Chartreuse as the tree of happiness
Chartreuse as the sea of glass
Chartreuse as the dolphin's treasure
Chartreuse as the secret ruins
Chartreuse as the peak's view
Chartreuse as the water whirlwind
Chartreuse as the Phoenix's friend
Chartreuse as the unstable underworld
Chartreuse as the crystal's cry
Chartreuse as the second sorrow
Chartreuse as all

Dashiell Kilpatrick, Grade 4
Fair Oaks School, Los Angeles County
Ericka Irwin, Classroom Teacher
Alice Pero, Poet-Teacher

Ukraine, Yellow and Blue

Yellow and blue are the colors of war.
Yellow and blue are the colors of Ukraine.
I believe I could stop the battle.
I could run off and bring help and they would survive.
I would lie on my bed with a fire in my head.
I believe all my hopes will come true.
I am yellow as a sunflower, the flower of Ukraine.

Clara Robinson, Grade 2
Alexander Valley School, Sonoma County
Sarah Sheehy, Classroom Teacher
Maureen Hurley, Poet-Teacher

Light

That gold ball catching my eye,
drowning me in like a hawk
to the sun. That midnight sky cusping
above the trees, the meadows
that were once green, now gray.
Small dots, trickles
of white coming down
shooting across the sky.
That big orange orb goes down,
the gold dust flies through the air
like a fox running
through a field of daisies,
his coat so vibrant like my night-light
trying to wake me up at night.

Bella Andorson, Grade 8
Mattole School, Humboldt County
Kevin Vesely, Classroom Teacher
Dan Zev Levinson, Poet-Teacher

One Word

One word is all it takes
One word can change everything
One word can stop the wars and fighting
One word can help the Russians and Ukrainians from death
One word can clear your mind
One word can take you to a different place
One word can change your relationship with someone close
One word can create the strings of the universe
One word can save a life
One word can make someone feel something new

One word is stronger than you think—
      any word can change anything,
      can change your feelings for someone

One word, as simple as yes
      or perhaps a no
      that's all it takes –
      just one simple word...

One word can change who you are,
can change everyone and everything.
Words so soft and so hurtful can change you,
can change me, no matter what word, it is strong.

Any words can be hurtful or meaningful, no matter what
All words you hear and say will always affect someone,
whether happy, sad, angry, or devastating,

Words can do so much more than you think.

Eleanor Gaida Ceccarelli, Grade 5
Oak Grove Elementary School, Sonoma County
Amanda Borges, Classroom Teacher
Brennan DeFrisco, Poet-Teacher

I Am Offering This Poem

after Jimmy Santiago Baca

I am offering this poem
If you need something to eat
I am offering this poem
If you need a place to sleep
I am offering this poem
If you need somewhere to live
I am offering this poem
I have nothing else to give.

Abigail Kruger, Grade 4
Alexander Valley School, Sonoma County
Nadia Podesto, Classroom Teacher
Maureen Hurley, Poet-Teacher

Poetry Is A Song

Poetry is like the sun setting against a sky.
Poetry is the pain that brings you relief.
It is the silver sun and the yellow moon.
It is the waves in the ocean, clear as glass.
But the currents underneath, hectic as your soul.
It is the black light and the bright soul.

Lorali Healy Wilson, Grade 2
Malcolm X Elementary, Alameda County
Dr. Kathryn Mapps, Classroom Teacher
Maureen Hurley, Poet-Teacher

Soul

The soul moves every time you grow.
It's any color you want it to be.
It is like a rose about to bloom under a ray of summer sunshine.
It rolls throughout the body like a lost bear that doesn't know
which way to go.
Soul locked away.
Soul with a thousand eyes.
Soul in the middle of winter with a million doors it could go
through, but it doesn't know which one to go through.
The soul can't do its ways when a human doesn't have pride.
What can it do without the things you need in life?
The soul and heart are what you need to live in life.
What your soul needs is what you need so take it, accept it.
Accept you.
Accept yourself.
And when the soul goes you go with it.
It shatters once you die.

Mason Boals, Grade 2
Malcolm X Elementary School, Alameda County
Jessica Arroyo, Jila Abdolhosseini, Classroom Teachers
Maureen Hurley, Poet-Teacher

Beyond My Bedroom

You sit in your room.
Hardly moving,
Hardly thinking.
You watch the television,
Your knees,
Your bookshelf, all seems fine right? No.
Just a few houses down a young girl is being
Yelled at by her father.
A couple blocks more, an unarmed man has been shot.
Dead. Gone.
You're unaware, aren't you?
Many hours away, a girl had to say goodbye to her father
as he went off to war.
As she waves at the train as he leaves,
you are just starting to doze off.
And when you wake up.
It's already getting too late...

Annika Jones, Grade 6
Coastal Grove Charter School, Humboldt County
Shana Langer, Classroom Teacher
Julie Hochfeld, Poet-Teacher

Silence Of The Defeated

Silence of the Defeated
Whose woes have conquered the world
Slashed their pride,
buried their dignity
Names of the warriors all in vain
Sorrow of thee unknown
Blood of the fallen seeps through the soil, blooming and dying
Mouths of babes cry for the milk of life
The angels are in sight
The trumpets have proclaimed
Darkness has arrived
Death, what sweet anticipation

Jessica Dominguez, Grade 11
Oxnard Middle College High School, Ventura County
Jennifer Brickey, Classroom Teacher
Fernando Albert Salinas, Poet-Teacher

Dread

As it rains, it drips of the sorrow once in your brain.
You held it in even when it was aching to come through.
Let me rise and stretch so I don't mature into a fuzz like you.
You show your colors as the rain drips down deep enough
To pass your dark and eerie body.
If you hurt so much, why make others feel your pain?
The rainbow which soon faded away symbolized your childish
Needs that got pushed away.
You know you crumble each day, but manipulate yourself
Into something you hope never stays.
If you feel your aches of dread why not say,
"I'm sorry I make you feel this way."
I feel no remorse not even guilt, but I know once I stay
Still and let the rush come through
It all stops and shows what I have been craving
They made me who I was, but won't accept me
For whom I'm soon going to be.
If you're the light and I'm the darkness why must our similarities
Be so far?
I show you the side of vulnerability I don't even see myself.
But you take my wrenching words and turn it into
Something about you.

Isabella Bozzi, Grade 8
Rancho Santana School, San Benito County
Carly Obertello, Classroom Teacher
Amanda Chiado, Poet-Teacher

Anger

Something's wrong.
Your teeth grind.
Your fists clench.
Something wants to make you roar.
You feel like you're on fire
like a stormy sea.
Your forehead burns.
You strike like lightening
and rumble like thunder.
You feel like a winter blizzard.
Like an oven.
You blow shards of ice
with your fierce winds.
You are slowly heating up,
getting ready to burn.
You feel like a baseball bat.
Like a waiting flytrap.
The ball comes fast,
but you eat it up.
You're waiting for
the right time to snap.
You feel like a lantern fish.
Like drums.
You hold your light
in front of you and
wait for your prey.
Your heart beats out
a rhythm.

You feel like you're eating
chili peppers.
Like a charging bull.
The spice crawls to your tongue
as you try to spit it out.
You wait for the red,
then charge toward your victim.
This
teeth grinding,
fist clenching
growling,
thumping,
roaring,
burning,
storming,
rumbling,
blowing,
heating,
hitting,
snapping,
waiting,
charging,
itching,
maddening,
anger.

Eva Pulliam, Grade 4
Edna McGuire School, Marin County
Ann Eshoff, Classroom Teacher
Claire Blotter, Poet-Teacher

Dreadful Memories

I hate you, math, with all my heart.
I suffer in agony thinking of you
and going through dreadful reminiscence
and anxiety rushing through my head.

My memories being flooded with horrible
memories I cannot forget, thinking of fear,
pain, and sadness when I think of you.

Agony is what I feel every
time I have to face you.

Math, I hate you, I really do.
You've cut me down, made me cry, frustrated,
and as a result, I fear you. I still do.
With all my heart, I know that I will never
win this battle.

Math, I know that I can never escape
your grasp.

As I am in your grasp,
I try to escape it.
I try and I try, but to no avail.
I stumble, I trip,
and I tremble with
your equations.

As I see some
light shining from above,
it will be soon that I escape
from your torture.
June 8th is when
I will be set free,
but until then, I
will still see you
looking at me.

And when the time comes,
I will be full of joy escaping
for a short period of time.
That is a small break
of two months.

And when high school comes around,
I know that I will not have fun .
learning about you, I will be
full of stress and worries, and that I will endure
four years of suffering.

Alexander Lozano, Grade 8
Rancho Santana School, San Benito County
Carly Obertello, Classroom Teacher
Amanda Chiado, Poet-Teacher

To Your Parent or Guardian

This letter has been sent to address
~~how rude your child has been, very rude~~
It is very unruly and needs to stop immediately.
~~We have had many instances of rudeness.~~
Here are a few suggestions for how to stop your child
    1. ~~Give a reward if the child stops being rude~~
    2. ~~Get a new child~~
    3. ~~Replace child~~

Caden Demers, Grade 7
Coastal Grove Charter School, Humboldt County
Jenny Rushby, Classroom Teacher
Julie Hochfeld, Poet-Teacher

No Dinner

Dear Hunger—

If I could corner you in a room filled
with hamburgers
I would ask you
why you make my life so hard
and why do you starve me?
If you were a landscape
You'd be an empty restaurant,
You would have red ketchup hair,
hamburger and fry eyes
and a meat filled face
You sound like someone chewing
with their mouth open
You taste like a rotten piece of meat
You smell like cheesy nachos
on the table aside me
You feel like something I wish I never had.

Kayley Medina, Grade 5
Arena Elementary School, Mendocino County
Rebecca Willhoit, Classroom Teacher
Blake More, Poet-Teacher

Worry

Worry is a thick mysterious forest
with who knows how many dangers.
Worry's best friends are uncertainties—
they make you feel scared.
Worry is the war between Russia
and Ukraine, not knowing if you
will be alive in the morning.
Worry is Grandma getting
cancer last year.
Worry is the frightful orthodontist
giving you braces.
Worry is storm clouds waiting
for the right moment to explode.

Natalie Balderrama, Grade 4
Loma Verde School, Marin County
Dayla Greenfield, Classroom Teacher
Claire Blotter, Poet-Teacher

Mindless Minds

I feel like I could
never be free
I never want to
feel this way
My mindless mind could
never be filled

I could never
be heard
Nobody could understand me
I hide and never come out
Deep down I could never be saved
No one could ever see the real me

People don't notice or
say anything
Freedom is a dream
that I could never fulfill
My mind can never let go
of my past

Memories run through my mind
hurt and happiness
I try to yell but
nothing comes out
No emotions on my face

I see people around me
not knowing what to do

I go crazy but
I could never go anywhere
Loneliness is my unwanted friend

Jennavie Robles, Grade 8
Rancho Santana School, San Benito County
Carly Obertello, Classroom Teacher
Amanda Chiado, Poet-Teacher

Love Isn't Always What You Think

Love, you might think of romantic love
When you hear the word love
But there are so many types of love
There's family love, self-love, and toxic love
You see, love isn't always what you think
It's dangerous and adventurous
You see, love can hurt you in so many ways
To the point where you feel like you're fading away
Love is confusing because your scared to get hurt
But you want to love again
Love can make you do so many crazy things
Like changing yourself for that person you love
There are so many different purposes of love in a person's life
You might feel alone but just know,
There are many other people that feel the same way you do
So don't be scared to love again
Just know you'll find love once again,
You're going to love multiple people and get your heart broken
        over and over again
But just keep in mind, in the end
You'll realize
That you had to love multiple people
and get hurt multiple times
to find your true love.

Brielle Jaquias, Grade 8
Rancho Santana School, San Benito County
Carly Obertello, Classroom Teacher
Amanda Chiado, Poet-Teacher

Pretty Is A Lie

There is very little truth in beauty,
just as there is very little beauty in the truth.
We are conditioned to embrace lies
and the judgement of our peers.
It isn't right.

We dress up our skeletons
as if we aren't going to grow old at some point.
We pretend what we look like really matters.
We made this fake competition.
This competition where everyone competes.
This competition where nobody ever wins,
and yet there's still losers.
It's a steeplechase. A drag-race.
A high speed, cross country, statewide police chase.
Honestly, it's a disgrace.
This thinking system must be replaced.

The price of being caught without layers and layers of "beauty"
is a life sentence.
One person sees you with a face that is bare,
and they become your judge and jury.
You beg for forgiveness and promise repentance.
They make you face the crowd, the census.
We watch and compare.
We show and share.
We take selfies and post them as if we hadn't doctored them up,
like a surgeon performing a heart transplant.

Just trying to hide the scars,
the scars of our attempts for perfect
because we aren't pretty or worthy until a stranger clicks Like.
Looking for pretty and perfection,
looking for perfection as if it truly exists.
Is perfection really just searching for acceptance and affection?
I think that is a real question.

We learned it from society, perhaps our mothers and fathers,
our uncles and aunts. we've been searching for it all our lives,
like a blind pirate looking for the lost treasure,
yet we can't find the map.
We put others down for not altering their appearance.
We've been boarding up the most hated parts of ourselves
as if being content with who you truly are
is more unnatural than changing every little detail for the accepted
pretty of life.

As if you must find flaws in everything you see in yourself.
As if you mustn't be confident with who you are.
As if there is no way you can be accepted if you don't change.
As if you can't just be... yourself
because despite the makeup and the muscle,
the hair and the clothes,
you are still you.

You still have your thoughts and your past.
You still have your opinions and judgement.
your gifts, your cares, your talents.
finding true joy in what you love

you just being you.
That is truth and that is pretty.

Roman Bell, Grade 12
Oxnard High School, Ventura County
Marcell Brickey, Classroom Teacher
Fernando Albert Salinas, Poet-Teacher

Courage

Courage wears blue jeans with a vest that is loose on her
Her hair is in a bun.
She understands the language of sweat and monsters.
She was born in a dark den
exactly when a wolf howled.
Her best friends are risk and the stars.
Her job is fighting children's monsters and climbing sheer cliffs,
　　　never an ice cream man.
She hunts with wolves and there is always a payoff.
She lives in a damp cave with bears and skunks.
She dreams of someday skydiving, that free falling feeling.
Courage.
Courage.
Oh, I am courage.

Alexandra Le Renard, Grade 4
Montecito Union School, Santa Barbara County
Megan Soderborg, Classroom Teacher
Cie Gumucio, Poet-Teacher

Curiosity

A bright yellow with white polka dots.
A boy with a brown button up with a yellow tie.
Hair in a messy man bun, ready for exploration.
He sleeps in a box, with everything he needs.
Food, water, a trumpet, a bike and his precious old camera.
Curiosity walks through the city, capturing everything he sees.
Born in a science lab, Son of Confusion and Intelligence.
Walking in his red shoelaces with the white tip.
He carries his trumpet along with him everywhere he goes.
His bicycle doesn't have a horn, so you can see him blasting
        through the crowd!
Hrmmmmmmmmk! says the trumpet.
Curiosity owns a pair of blue and yellow roller skates.
Sometimes he goes to the local roller rink to take retro photos.
After a long day, Curiosity goes back to his box.
He sets up his camera into an angle where the night sky
is the only thing you see between the buildings.
Because he has always wondered what earth is like at night.

Sarah Martiny, Grade 6
Mountain View Elementary, Santa Barbara County
Anna Strenk, Classroom Teacher
Cie Gumucio, Poet-Teacher

Stars

Stars are celestial beings.
We see them as lights in the sky.
We see them as though they are always there,
always on, always bright.
Always shining with all the strength they can muster.
But sometimes they go out, sometimes they dim.
Those stars become faint.
Distant. Untouchable.
Unable to come out of their tightly compacted shells.
Because those stars have feelings.
They reach out, touching every corner of every galaxy.
Reaching. Feeling.
They try to grasp at every little piece of knowledge.
Try to find the answer to every question.
Every puzzle, every problem.
But sometimes they hide, they retreat, withdrawing from the
       pressure of the universe
They are scared, hurt, confused.
And this is when a bright star comes.
They light up the dim ones, bring them out of their shells.
Help them.
Bring back the light that has been missing for far too long.
This creates a ripple effect.
Stars ignite others, who bring radiance to others, and so on,
So, they can shine bright as well.
Because we are *all* celestial beings.

Camille Saneholtz, Grade 5
Oak Grove Elementary, Sonoma County
Tom Genolio, Classroom Teacher
Brennan DeFrisco, Poet-Teacher

Never Stop Believing

I believe that a cry of a child is carried in the autumn breeze.
That a book can change the way you think about the world.
That you can leave your room without really leaving.
I believe you can change the world by doing little things.
You can smell the roses on the verge of blooming.
That death is true and we cannot deny it.
I believe that you don't have to stop believing.
That a bird sings a song just for you.
That streams can become big rivers.
I believe in the summer air that carries the howl of the lone wolf.
That we hurt others without intending to.
We have scars on our hearts that are as big as the universe.
I DON'T believe that the child's cry is sad and remorseful, but
happy and content.
I DON'T believe that we stop believing.
I DON'T believe that we will always have scars on our hearts that
are as big as the universe.
I believe that believing is a treasure
and if you can find it, use it as much as you can.

Eleanor Abell, Grade 5
Arcata Elementary School, Humboldt County
Nicole Reis, Classroom Teacher
Dan Zev Levinson, Poet-Teacher

Inspiration

I need to write a poem.
But what should I write about?
I could do:
A poem about a pet, a dog or a cat
A poem about a sport, basketball or soccer
A poem about school, math or science
A poem about fortune, raining money and gold
A poem about a storm, thunder and lightning
A poem about having superpowers, invisibility or flight
A poem about seeing the future, what could go wrong?
A poem about needing inspiration...
Oh! That's a good idea.
But what should I write about?

Sam Clifton, Grade 7
Coastal Grove Charter School, Humboldt County
Jenny Rushby, Classroom Teacher
Julie Hochfeld, Poet-Teacher

My Scope of Imagination

I am the crashing waves
Of the Mediterranean sea
The deep exhilarating blue that flows
I am the scope of imagination
That seeps in when the white soft clouds
Hover over the bawling sunset of harmonious colors;
Am I the profound sad hymns of the sea that
Guide a sailor lost at glee
Am I the collapsing stars in our
expanding universe,
The one star whom you make
A promise to
I am freedom and the possibility of everything
Whatever that may be;
I am glad not to be the thin sheet
Of water lying on the concrete
I am glad not to be another sheep
Following the herd
I am glad to be the dance the brings golden happiness
To this one world

Penelope Aprile, Grade 9
Lowell High School, San Francisco County
Sam Williams, Classroom Teacher
Susan Terence, Poet-Teacher

Not Lost Are The Stories

Poet-Teacher Poems

Advice to My Students

My students eyebrow dialogue
as I tack the jumbo infant photo
on the white board.

What's that? they shout.
Who has a baby sister or brother? I ask.
Three hands go up.

How does an infant take in the world?
They put everything in their mouth
and stare at you, a boy blurts.

Look at her eyes, her mouth, I say
study the grasping fingers
of a being

whose life is driven
by the need to understand.
Be *that baby.*

For this hour, forget
about Warcraft and skate parks,
Avengers, and the latest Batman movie.

Watch the oak tree's branches
graze the sky.
Listen to the trilling of Redwings.

What do they tell you?
Look at a rock with new eyes.
Set it on your palm and trace its ridges.

Return to the time
when everything you touched
filled you with wonder or delight.

Recess is coming.
Pokémon will wait.

Sandra Anfang
Poet-Teacher, Sonoma County

Autumn Chicano

Autumn, the Chicano season
The time where the earth browns and goldens
Much like the skin tone of my many brothers and sisters
When the breeze helps remind us of the dead
Only to find comfort in the warm soups and festive bread
When we begin to gather supplies to last through winter
When every craving is met with satisfaction
When we plan to leave and promise to come back
Mama said, "El comida es mejor con familia"
With crazy Tías to give the sour taste
And grumpy Tíos to feed the fuel
Balance with sweet cousins and juicy chisme
We feel the warmth like a nicely wrapped tamale
We feel united but still divided
Autumn is a Chicano feeling fulfilled

Vincent T Jimenez
Poet-Teacher, Ventura County

Spring's Reckoning

As I walk the neighborhood,
I capture a pair of bluebirds
flitting from treetop to treetop
and I am instantly elevated into the
blue of spring sky, into the hope
of warmth after a winter
filled with rain-soaked days—
a dampness that made
my bones chill.

Two days ago, off Hwy 199,
the road I frequently travel,
a couple sat inside their car
when a redwood toppled over
crashing the roof,
crushing both of them.

They were tourists just passing through
like the bluebirds that come only
in spring. What orchestrates such fate?
The timing impeccable for death
or the timing for
the burst of magnolia blossoms
and little birds with the bluest of wings?

My heart keeps pumping blue blood
through its thick arteries,
a map full of dangerous bends

like this highway that sidewinds
through towering trees.
But I am still here to witness
the wing beat of bluebirds,
the lilacs budding & poppies blooming.

Just down the road, the redwoods
are murmuring about their relative
when his roots lost grip
from rain drenched soil.

Terri Glass
Poet-Teacher, Marin County

Lost Are The Trees

Lost are the trees
tearing a hole in the sky
Lost are the trees
shading caked earth

Lost are the trees
our tiny hands touched,
peeling off bark
and climbed

Lost is the house once
surrounded by trees
Lost is the house
built from earth

Lost is the house where
we ate, slept, consoled,
comforted, cried

Lost is the house of
our childhood

full of odd shoes
and boxes, and fabric
made into dresses,
scraps into quilts

Lost is the mother,
seamstress, chef,

who planted the garden
asparagus, mulberries,
strawberries, grapes

Lost is the mother
who saved
every seed
Lost are apricots
at sunset begun by seed,
dry peaches at noon,
burst pomegranates

Lost is the gardener
Lost is the bed
we sat on

(Not lost are the
stories)

Lost all together
trees, dirt walls,
shoes, and the seeds
all the seeds she planted

(Not lost are the stories)

How the trees touching
mountains
started small as
the palm of a hand

how she plucked chickens
under the trees

how she grew strawberries
where once there were chickens

how acres of apricots, peaches
and cantaloupes became
pies became everything

the color of our memory

how we can no longer visit
because she is not there
and the house is not there
and the trees are not there
and the loss is too large
to visit

Susan Terence
Poet-Teacher, San Francisco County

What I Left Behind

I lost my home on a smoky night
trunk crammed with art and photographs
bereft of what I left behind
wisteria, foxglove, silk kimono
erased, reduced to elemental carbon
I lost my home on a mountainside
where fire scaled this rocky ridge
to scald my skies in ochre
a ritual of renunciation
I lost my home to a seething wind
that taught me how to breathe again
the final chapter of who I had been

Michele Krueger
Poet-Teacher, Lake County

Balancing Act

Obscene, contorted, thick weeping-beech-branch-veins bulge.
The vascularity of his extended arm is grotesque.
His frostbitten fingers tremble beneath the weight of silence.

Silence is the saddest song—deafening.
Deadweight is exhausting—miserable.

He holds his beatless heart.

The silhouette of a crocodile-headed monstrosity
with an ostrich feather pinched in its teethy grin
stirs void. This is no time for a balancing act.
The man keeps one hand hidden behind his back.

Fernando Albert Salinas
Poet-Teacher, Ventura County

What's Making That Sound?

It's me making that sound
not a ghost nor a katydid

It's me clicking my tongue on my teeth
to feel sound in my mouth,

sound as round as the top of a bell
the cool curve you brush your thumb over

It's the rhythm I love the counterpoint
to heartbeat and breath

the range of possible sounds I can make
with my teeth and my tongue and my mouth

Who needs musical instruments when you can pop
plink shout and let out symphonies
inside you?

Just imagine and try clicking your teeth sometime
like I'm doing now (click click)
with my tongue

Claire Blotter
Poet-Teacher, Marin County

Tolerance is Bliss

We abide this ledge of cosmos
the micro macro
or macro micro
of ocean roar and redwood

We are a tall order
under remote lens
confronted every day by the sheer beauty of ourselves
fox cries echoing through the wind
a mountain lion darting along the perimeter
hummingbird showering beneath garden sprayer

We are the whales, hawks, bears and deer
the gathering squirrels and naked ladies
of day
the owls and howls of night
we shoot like stars
and rest like ravens

We pulse land and water
through our bodies
individually and collectively
we resonate
as we deliver groceries
fix the leak
raise the barn
speed from the hospital

Alone and together
we mirror the whole
weeks of solitude reflected in ocean wave
and cumulative understanding
we are this earth
and this earth is holding us up
even when we gnash our teeth and forget to breathe

The screen inside our mind is not a goal
inhaling is a goal
exhaling its reward
one moment unfolding the way it does
seamless stitches
into this spell of choices

Some call it about time
I call it a circle
no end, no beginning
just one continuous flow
offerings from turquoise sea
stretched out below
inviting, diving
cavernous and calm,
churning tumult, a world away

this inner tending is our green peace
self-care activism
revealing vast constellations and wild animals inside

we are waking up
walking along the deep steep

juking and dodging the questions
as they insist like rain
into a thirsty mouth

soon we will realize
we are the answers
as we find new ways
to watch, learn, listen, share
touch our double helix
and reclaim it
with our lives

Blake More
Poet-Teacher, Mendocino County

The Apricot Tree

so much depends upon
     the orange apricots

and the old man
     who tends the tree

gives away
     bags of fruit

and loves me

an old man
     more frail each year

whom I hug
     never knowing if

it will be
     the last

until it is

Julie Hochfeld
Poet-Teacher, Humboldt County

Cumulonimbus

Do you know what it means to be water?
To be many forms & nothing more
than one thing? To be desert stream
& frozen lake & raincloud at the
same time? To sublimate
when your heart doesn't feel
like melting, becoming the wind instead?
To be last breath, watching the rest
become too heavy to hold water?

All water evaporates naturally
& we are all made of water
& we are all becoming
the wind.

Brennan DeFrisco
Poet-Teacher, Alameda & Sonoma County

Oh, Wind

for Pádraig Ó Tuama

Oh, wind, with your restless hands
rippling the deep grasses on the hillsides,
your invisible corpse suppressing the morning fog
until it flops over like a cat wanting a belly rub,
your breath pleating the hems of a lake
or fanning the wildfires scorching the earth
until we succumb to detachment,
until there is no other choice left except now.
Oh, wind, bring me detachment,
bring me a place of no boundaries
because we daily drown in the detritus of dailiness
and sometimes we forget the larger picture.
Bring me no countries, no alliances,
until we are no longer earthbound.
Oh, let me be more like the birds of prey
circling updrafts and searching for a pattern
larger than the confines of the mind.
May it be.

Maureen Hurley
Poet-Teacher, Alameda & Sonoma County

In The Be

Breathe
In Be GEN Sing.
Black BA-LAM BOOOOOOM
Beep bop ear eye drop dream.
Trans lucent wings.
Reverent evanescent feathers
Favor Raven magic.
Tether star shine, clothed in
Glitter dark red yellow green
Purple gold mind.

Dance a spiral round root
Tally ground wire imbue
Re member, light seed deed.
Drum heart lung tongue stars
Rhythm sung long time gone.
Revolution's evolution
You and I verse, plans planets seat
Rock steady beat, arms legs feet
Wave weave in heat.

Moon mounts magnetic mystery
Bring back the Honey Bees, please
And swing low my sweet chariot
Let us ride home.

Heaven's sunflower
Has thrown us in this throne

of Halleluiah parallel strings
Orchestrating DNA's helix springs
Springing up children, prophets
Circulating circuits-trees
Generating generations of
Yin yang prophesy
Radicals radiating
I she' O' Lua
Coole' bahdeo.

The Word, 'Nummo'
Will not to be destroyed
In the Be Gen Sing.
G force spiraling
Cannot gainsay
Nor resist

Tureeda Mikell
Poet-Teacher, Alameda County

Bubble

This is my bubble ever growing
Here where silence, words and music
float
No limit
Are there millions, billions of thoughts?
They emerge one at a time
as though forgotten and then come back again
How many places?
a slide down a slope or race up
to where they live
an instant note, word or dance
a tiny slice of what I once knew
bursts forth
The force of nothing
the nothing of force
If there is silence, I will find that too
going where the Lord of All Things
might be
though I might be he (or she)
blown through space
Time blown
in the No Wind
of pure spirit energy

Alice Pero
Poet-Teacher, Los Angeles County

Thoughts On Poetry

inspired by the 6th Grade poetry students at
Mill Valley Middle School

Sometimes, you don't recognize there's a poem
      hidden deep down inside of you.
You don't know until you are soulfully quiet.
You don't know until you shut off all the mental chattering —
that inner voice that sounds like a cacophony of blue jays
      in the tall pines.
Sometimes, you just have to find a silent place to be able to hear
      the pure voice inside you.
The voice that is willing to be vulnerable, available,
      to share with the world.
Sometimes, words from the mind drift out in a tangle,
like kelp drifting in the ocean, knotted and constrained.
Sometimes, words flow effortlessly with no boundaries,
wide as the Amazon with no consideration, no constriction,
      no tightness.
They flow without ebb or moonlit tidal pull.
This is freedom.
This is when poetry is magic.

Michele Rivers
Poet-Teacher, Marin County

Acknowledgements

In The Be by Tureeda Mikell was first published in *The Maynard*

California Poets in the Schools extends our overwhelming gratitude to all the agencies, arts foundations, and contributors that made this publication possible, including the California Arts Council, the Poetry Foundation, and the Literary Arts Emergency Fund.

Special thanks to all the administrators, teachers, librarians, and literacy coaches who welcome our Poet-Teachers into their schools and classrooms. Thank you for providing and sharing the space for our poetry workshops.

Thank you to all the CalPoets coordinators and Poet-Teachers whose knowledge, facilitation and artistic guidance catalyzed the creation of this anthology and all the poems written beyond these pages.
Thank you for all you do.

A cacophony of applause to all our student poet contributors for sharing your words, your selves, and your literary brilliance with all of us through this collection. Thank you for you.

& thank you, reader, for spending time with these poems.

California Poets in the Schools' vision is to enable youth in every California county to discover, cultivate and amplify their own creative voices through reading, analyzing, writing, performing and publishing poetry. When students learn to express their creativity, imagination, and intellectual curiosity through poetry, it becomes a catalyst for learning core academic subjects, accelerating emotional development and supporting personal growth. Our Poet-Teachers help students become adults who will bring compassion, understanding and appreciation for diverse perspectives to dialogue about issues which their communities face.

California Poets in the Schools (CalPoets) develops and empowers a multicultural network of independent Poet- Teachers, who bring the many benefits of poetry to youth throughout the state. As a membership network we offer opportunities for professional development, peer learning and fundraising assistance for Poet-Teachers in California. We also cultivate relationships with school districts, foundations and arts organizations which can fund and support our members' professional practices.

Since 1964, CalPoets has grown to become one of the oldest and largest writers-in-the-schools programs in the nation. Our reach includes 20,000 students served annually by 100 Poet-Teachers from throughout California. Poet-Teachers live and serve students K-12 in over 30 California counties, stretching from Humboldt and Siskiyou to Los Angeles and San Diego, in districts both urban and rural. Each year CalPoets' Poet-Teachers reach hundreds of classrooms, teaching in public and private schools, juvenile halls, after-school programs, hospitals and other community settings.

CalPoets champions and amplifies the voices of California youth by providing platforms for critical literacy, youth development & leadership through school-based poetry writing, publication and performance opportunities.

To Contact CalPoets for a residency:

Phone – 1-415-221-4201
Email – info@cpits.org
Website – www.californiapoets.org

.

CPSIA information can be obtained
at www.ICGtesting.com
Printed in the USA
JSHW051413251122
33485JS00003BA/9